FIRST PAST THE PO

English:
COMPREHENSIONS

Book 2
Contemporary Literature
Tests 1 - 10

How to use this pack to make the most of 11 plus exam preparation

It is important to remember that for 11 plus exams there is no national syllabus, no pass mark and no retake option! It is therefore vitally important that your child is fully primed to perform to the best of their ability so that they give themselves the best possible chance on the day.

Unlike similar publications, the **First Past The Post®** series uniquely assesses your child's performance on a question-by-question basis, helping to identify areas for improvement and providing suggestions for further targeted tests.

English Comprehension

This collection of tests is representative of the standard comprehension section of contemporary multi-discipline 11 plus exams, including those set by CEM (Durham University). Each test contains a variety of question styles that are common across grammar and independent school exams. Typically, questions test the student's ability to extract factual information, draw inferences, and use their own judgement or reasoning skills in order to interpret the extract. In addition, some questions test the student's knowledge of vocabulary, grammar and literary techniques. The suggested time for each test is based on data obtained from conventional classroom testing sessions.

Never has it been more useful to learn from mistakes!

Students can improve by as much as 15% not only by focused practice but also by targeting any weak areas.

How to manage your child's practice

To get the most up-to-date information, visit the Eleven Plus Exams website. Eleven Plus Exams is the largest UK online resource with over 40,000 webpages and a forum administered by a select group of experienced moderators. (www.elevenplusexams.co.uk)

About the authors

The Eleven Plus Exams' **First Past The Post®** series has been created by a team of experienced tutors and authors from leading British universities including Oxford and Cambridge.

Published by University of Buckingham Press

With special thanks to the children who tested our material at the Eleven Plus Exams centre in Harrow.

ISBN: 9781908684486

Copyright © ElevenPlusExams.co.uk 2014

Contents

This workbook comprises ten comprehensions made up of 15 questions each, and each should take 12 minutes to complete.

Once you have completed each test and marked it using the answers at the back you can anonymously go online and compare your child's performance relative to peers who have completed the same test(s) using our 11+ Peer Compare System™.

Register at http://peercompare.elevenplusexams.co.uk/
and then activate the access code printed on the inside cover.

Instructions

For each question, mark your answer by drawing a firm horizontal line in the box next to your chosen option on the question sheet:

1. This is an example question.

    ⬭ a. Wrong answer
    ⬭ b. Wrong answer
    ⬭ c. Wrong answer
    ⬛ d. Right answer
    ⬭ e. Wrong answer

Use the method suggested below for working through comprehension papers:

i.   Always **read through the extract first**, you should not go straight to the questions.

ii.   **Do not skim-read,** your first reading should be sufficiently thorough so that you have a good understanding of the passage and can answer the questions more quickly and accurately. Otherwise, you are unlikely to have sufficient time available.

iii.   You should **underline key information** (e.g. names of characters, places, dates, events or key words that provide an explanation of the subject matter) as this will help you to navigate the passage and recall the main points, especially where the question does not provide line references. Be careful not to let the underlining slow down your reading or distract you from understanding what you are reading.

iv.   Read the questions and then **refer back to the text** in order to find the relevant answers. If you underlined key words and read thoroughly, then you should be able to easily find the relevant parts of the passage that you need to refer back in order to find the answer.

v.   There are broadly **four main types of question** as shown in the table opposite. Remember, some questions might be a combination of these different types.

To mark your papers, use the 'Answers' section at the back of this booklet. The mark scheme will give you the correct answer option, as well as a short explanation of how each question should have been worked out.

For content-based questions, line references are provided pointing you to the location of the answer in the text.

For other types of questions, the mark scheme states whether inference, judgement or knowledge was required to arrive at the right answer.

Where relevant, line references are also provided for inference and judgement questions to indicate where the text hints at the answer.

Comprehension questions fall into four main types, as shown in the table below:

Type	Where/how to find the answer	Example(s)
Factual content	Specifically stated in the text	Given a text that explains 'When Sophie was 11, she had a terrible accident', you might be asked how old Sophie was at the time of her accident. The answer will be specifically stated in the text.
Logical inference	Not directly stated in the text, but can be inferred (understood) from the details given	Given a text that describes the setting as 'cold, snowy and dark', you might be asked what season it is in the story or to identify true/false statements. You must use the hints given in the passage to work out the most likely answer.
Personal judgement	Not directly stated in the text; you must read more deeply into the text to form your own opinion	You may be asked to describe the feelings or reactions of a character or about the intentions of the author (e.g. What was Tommy's mood on his first day at school?). You must read between the lines and look at the language and tone used to form your own opinion.
Knowledge of grammar, vocabulary and literary techniques	Not stated in the text at all; you must use your knowledge to answer the question	Questions may ask about word meanings or ask you to recognise literary techniques such as alliteration and onomatopoeia. Be careful with vocabulary questions - all answers options may provide a correct definition of a word, but only one will fit the context of the passage.

Other titles in the First Past The Post® Series

11 + Essentials CEM Style Practice Tests

Verbal Reasoning: Cloze Tests
Book 1
9781908684288

Verbal Reasoning: Cloze Tests
Book 2
9781908684356

Verbal Reasoning: Grammar and
Spelling Multiple Choice Books 1 & 2
9781908684646 | 9781908684790

Verbal Reasoning: Vocabulary
Multiple Choice Books 1 & 2
9781908684639 | 9781908684783

Numerical Reasoning: Multi-part
Books 1 & 2
9781908684301 | 9781908684363

Numerical Reasoning: Multi-part
(Multiple Choice) Books 1 & 2
9781908684769 | 9781908684776
NEW for 2016

Numerical Reasoning: Quick-fire
Books 1 & 2
9781908684431 | 9781908684448

Numerical Reasoning: Quick-fire
(Multiple Choice) Books 1 & 2
9781908684653 | 9781908684752
NEW for 2016

English: Comprehensions
Book 1
9781908684295

English: Comprehensions
Book 2
9781908684486

3D Non-Verbal Reasoning
Book 1
9781908684318

3D Non-Verbal Reasoning
Book 2
9781908684479

Mental Arithmetic
Book 1
9781908684462

Numerical
Reasoning: Worded
Problems Book 1
9781908684806
NEW for 2016

Maths Dictionary Plus
9781908684493
NEW for 2016

11 + Practice Paper Packs

Non-Verbal Reasoning
Practice Papers
9781908684134

English
Practice Papers
9781908684103

Verbal Reasoning
Practice Papers
9781908684127

Mathematics
Practice Papers
9781908684110

Flynn (Test 1)

Marking Grid															
Question	1	2	3	4	5	6	7	8	9	10	11	12	13	14	15	Total
✓ or ✗																

Read the following instructions carefully:

1. You have 12 minutes to complete this test of 15 questions.

2. You are recommended to spend 5 minutes reading the text, and 7 minutes answering the questions.

3. Work as quickly and as carefully as you can.

4. When you have finished a page, continue straight on to the next page. Do not waste time.

5. You can write on the text itself, or use the available space on the question paper to do any working. However, only mark your final answer in the answer boxes.

6. Mark your answer using a pencil, by drawing a firm horizontal line in the box next to your chosen option.

7. To change an answer, rub out your original answer completely and then mark on your new choice.

8. If you cannot answer a question, go on to the next question.

9. When you have completed the paper, use the time remaining to go back to any questions you have missed out and check your answers.

Good luck!

'Flynn'

BREATHING heavily, Fran eagerly hauled her legs up the last small slope to the cairn, one booted foot at a time. Forcefully swinging her arms to gain as much momentum as she could, she made steady progress up the last few feet. As her booted foot finally made its final step to the top of the cairn, she stopped and
5 stared in awe at the picturesque landscape. The sun had made its way past the soft, pillowy clouds, to its throne at the top of the sky and illuminated the beautiful hummock in front of her and the vast valley to her below.

Satisfied and grinning, Fran placed her hands on her hips and surveyed the path in front of her. It was traced out in white and well-worn by scores of
10 fell-walkers' boots that had trudged doggedly along it for so many years. It beckoned her onwards, every bend and stretch reassuringly guiding her in what could only be the right direction: upwards towards the high tops of the hills. The summits ahead soared gloriously over the insignificant valleys below and stretched up high, curling their gentle fingers over the familiar curves of
15 the hillside, as old friends entwined in a fond embrace.

Fran glanced back, at the path where her father had just reached the bottom of that small yet onerous slope that led to where she now proudly stood. She looked forwards again, up towards the mighty summit of Raise and down at the meagre Sticks Gill that ran merrily along its base, bubbling happily over
20 stones and branches that were strewn over its winding path. Fran closed her eyes and breathed in, allowing the fresh, clean air to seep in through her nose and fill her lungs. A smile of pure, unadulterated happiness spread across her glowing face.

Relaxed and content, she focused her attention on the greatly anticipated
25 biscuit break that she had been promising herself for the last mile.

"I'm opening the custard creams," she called to her father, who had breached the top of the cairn. "Do you want one?"

"No, thanks," he gestured a weak thumbs-up and turned to take in the view, exhaling heavily in the crisp morning air. "Wow! That's quite a view." Reaching
30 instinctively into the back pocket of his jeans, he pulled out his camera and began adding to the already vast collection of pictures he'd taken that morning.

Fran eagerly selected the comfiest looking rock, flung her backpack off her shoulders and settled down against the cool, hard stone. She glanced behind

35 and took a moment to admire her morning's achievement before looking ahead to review the climb still to come.

A sudden scratching sound of falling scree, erupted from the edge of the path, accompanied by a short, sharp shout that echoed boldly around the hilltop. Fran glanced to the left and watched in horror as her father tumbled over the
40 side of the track and disappeared from view.

She sprang up and ran to the edge; where she peered frantically down the steep, sloping side of the deep valley, searching for her father's familiar face. Her father was about ten feet below her, sprawled untidily across the dislodged scree, his feet pointing downwards and his limbs spread-eagled,
45 desperately searching for a firm grip on the intractable surface. The scree continued to slip beneath his hands further and further, but he kept on clutching and clawing at the gravel to maintain his position and keep from falling any further down.

"DAD!?" she shouted wildly, as panic flooded her senses and paralysed her
50 body stock-still.

"Yep." He forced a monosyllabic, strained sound out of his chest. Every muscle in his body was taut with tension and he held his breath in a futile attempt to prevent another abrupt landslide of the rock.

Fran breathed a small sigh of relief and some of her panic subsided for a brief
55 second; but it quickly returned with renewed strength as she realised she was clueless as to what her next move may be. She shunted her right foot forward, in an unintentional bid to do something, anything proactive, and watched in horror as a fresh shower of rock plummeted in a powerful cascade down the steep slope, sending reverberations around the valley that quickly faded to soft
60 cracks as the rocks fell away far beneath them.

Fran murmured a terrified "Err.." mixed with a suppressed, panicked sob as her eyes flitted in a frenzied pattern across the scene below her, scanning in despair for anything that might hint at a half-baked plan. The turbulent state of the scree meant that any attempts she might make to physically help her
65 father would be futile, a few steps could cause him to fall even further down.

"What do I do?" she expelled in a shriek of alarm. Her emotions were in perpetual pandemonium; they flittered between the brink of wild hysteria and anger at herself, as it was she that decided they should go on a relaxing hike up. She looked down the valley, towards the civilisation they had left behind
70 and she wished it was not so far away.

"Don't… move… try to…" Her father's words were coming short and sharp, infused with mania and disbelief, as he continued to grasp wildly at the freely-sliding rock. His scuffed fingers alternated between clutched fists and open palms as he desperately tried to gain purchase on something solid.

75 Suddenly, Fran remembered the emergency pack in her rucksack. Half berating herself, half relieved, she snatched up her rucksack and delved frantically to retrieve her phone and the card of emergency numbers that she had heedfully placed.

"I'm going to get help!" she called over her shoulder, a new lease of energy
80 rushing through her body as a suggestion of a plan crept unassertively into her mind. She clutched at the new glimmer of hope gladly and acted immediately before another Pandora's box of doubts and terrors could burst open.

Her trembling fingers fumbled frenetically over the keys, punching in the number in wild desperation. Fran could hear her own heart beat twice the
85 speed of the ringback tone and finally, after what seemed like a year had gone by, a voice could be heard on the other end of the phone. She spluttered out her location in a rush of words and fast breaths, and fought with a rising urge to scream at the calm, slow voice at the other end of the crackly line. However, she knew that the clear, level-headed words of the operator at the mountain
90 rescue dog association were in fact indispensable and the only thing stopping her dad's situation from getting any worse. She put the phone down with an unsatisfying surge of relief and accomplishment and promptly sank despairingly to her knees as close to the edge of the path as she dared.

"They're coming. Hold on. Please hold on," she breathed feebly; conveying
95 what she hoped was a vaguely reassuring message to her father. He was still stranded hopelessly on the exposed hillside that stretched away beneath them.

Fran noticed the scene in front of her had become darker and glanced up to see a dark sky. Dense, black clouds hovered menacingly over the ridge of hills
100 and the head of the valley. They seemed to growl with malicious intent as they curled their dark talons around the edges of the hills, wrapping them in a murderous grip. Harsh, stinging raindrops began to fall, soaking Fran's clothes and cementing them to her cold skin.

Fran waited. Her mind slowed to a grind and stopped; no thoughts passed
105 through its empty, cavernous channels, it was only conscious of the damp, cold sensation of the once vivid world around her.

A distant, self-assured bark sent insistent echoes around the hillside, followed a short while later by a soft, wet muzzle nudging her back affectionately and a merry jangle of metal tickling her ears. Distractedly, she turned to see a round, brass disc glinting beneath the rain; etched on it in broad, friendly type was the word 'Flynn'.

1. Which of the following is the best synonym for the word 'eager' (line 1)?
   - a. unwilling
   - b. meagre
   - c. reluctant
   - d. keen
   - e. earnest

2. 'Satisfied and grinning, Fran placed her hands on her hips and surveyed the path in front of her...' (lines 8-9)
   How is Fran feeling at this point in the story?
   - a. tired and triumphant
   - b. triumphant and pleased
   - c. hungry and happy
   - d. displeased and relieved
   - e. impatient and tired

3. '...as old friends entwined in a fond embrace.' (lines 15)
   What literary technique is prevalent in this phrase?
   - a. metaphor
   - b. onomatopoeia
   - c. simile
   - d. rhetoric
   - e. alliteration

4. What had Fran been looking forward to for the last mile of the walk?
   - a. a drink
   - b. a swim
   - c. a chat
   - d. a rest
   - e. a biscuit break

5. Where is Fran's father in relation to her when she asks if he wants a custard cream?
   - a. a little further back down the path
   - b. right next to her
   - c. a mile behind her
   - d. further ahead of her on the path
   - e. at the bottom of the mountain

6. At what time of day do they stop for the biscuit break?
- a. morning
- b. midday
- c. dawn
- d. afternoon
- e. twilight

7. What was Fran's father doing when he fell over the edge of the path?
- a. eating a custard cream
- b. talking to Fran
- c. balancing on the edge of the path
- d. taking photographs
- e. drinking water

8. '...a short, sharp shout...' (line 38)
   What literary technique is prevalent in this phrase?
- a. simile
- b. alliteration
- c. metaphor
- d. onomatopoeia
- e. repetition

9. What type of word is 'wildly' (line 49)?
- a. a noun
- b. a preposition
- c. a verb
- d. an adverb
- e. an adjective

10. Which of the following is the best definition for the word 'futile' (line 52)?
- a. desperate and unthinking
- b. unable to consider the consequences of an action
- c. incapable of producing a useful result
- d. attempting to plan for the future
- e. successful in achieving a particular aim

11. What plan does Fran have as she searches through her rucksack?
- a. She plans to throw some water and biscuits down to her father.
- b. She plans to use a rope that she has been carrying in her rucksack.
- c. She plans to call her mother to ask for advice.
- d. She plans to get out her first aid manual.
- e. She plans to call the mountain rescue dog association.

12. Which of the following best describes the voice at the end of the phone?
- a. high-pitched and hysterical
- b. composed and sensible
- c. angry and impatient
- d. bored and disinterested
- e. cool and smug

13. How have the clouds changed in lines 98-102 from that described at the beginning of the passage?
- a. They have changed from stormy to white.
- b. They have changed from rainy to snowy.
- c. They have disappeared.
- d. They have become thicker.
- e. They have changed from pleasant to threatening.

14. What is the 'damp, cold sensation' (line 105-106) that Fran feels?
- a. rain falling on her clothes
- b. sweat from the stress of the situation
- c. a dog's wet nose
- d. tears running down her cheeks
- e. snow on the ground

15. How is the arrival of Flynn intended to make the reader feel?
- a. happy and relieved
- b. confused and bewildered
- c. shocked and stunned
- d. worried and upset
- e. scared and anxious

Life at Nearly Six (Test 2)

Marking Grid															
Question	1	2	3	4	5	6	7	8	9	10	11	12	13	14	15	Total
✔ or ✘																

Read the following instructions carefully:

1. You have 12 minutes to complete this test of 15 questions.

2. You are recommended to spend 5 minutes reading the text, and 7 minutes answering the questions.

3. Work as quickly and as carefully as you can.

4. When you have finished a page, continue straight on to the next page. Do not waste time.

5. You can write on the text itself, or use the available space on the question paper to do any working. However, only mark your final answer in the answer boxes.

6. Mark your answer using a pencil, by drawing a firm horizontal line in the box next to your chosen option.

7. To change an answer, rub out your original answer completely and then mark on your new choice.

8. If you cannot answer a question, go on to the next question.

9. When you have completed the paper, use the time remaining to go back to any questions you have missed out and check your answers.

Good luck!

Once you have completed each test and marked it using the answers at the back you can anonymously go online and compare your child's performance relative to peers who have completed the same test(s) using our 11+ Peer Compare System™. Register at http://peercompare.elevenplusexams.co.uk/ and then activate the access code printed on the front inside cover of this book.

'Life at Nearly Six'

MY name is Isabella Thomas and I am five-and-three-quarters-years old. Even though I am the youngest in my class at school, my daddy says I am nearly a grown woman, and that's because I'm extra mature from having to take care of my little brother. He's only a one-year old, and he's really super tiny so I have to make sure he doesn't bash his head against the wall or fall down the stairs. It's very hard to save him from getting hurt because he likes to be silly, especially when he gets hyper. Once I told Daddy that I thought Michael was being too silly and needed to go on the naughty step but he just said 'Boys will be boys.' and put one eyebrow up. I don't really know what he meant because
10 I don't see how a boy could be a girl in any case but he gave me a cuddle when he said it, like he does when he's telling me an adult secret so I suppose I'll know what it means when I'm really truly a woman. Daddy likes to tell me little secrets. When I ask him how he knows these things, he says it's because he's wise like Dumbledore or Yoda or Santa Claus but I think he just means that it's
15 because he's old and wrinkly. I know he's old because he only has hair on the edge of his head and not in the middle.

I think my daddy is the smartest daddy in the world. He's got a very hard job because he's so smart. Sometimes when I wake up at night I go downstairs and I see him sitting at the table with his glasses and a frowny face on. He stares
20 and stares and stares at the teensy numbers on his computer screen and does speedy typing on the keyboard so it sounds like rain pat-a-pat-ing on the window. It seems like he finds his work really difficult. But the other day he opened his wallet to pay for the shopping and I saw he had more than five notes in there so he must make a lot of money, which is good.

25 The best thing about Daddy is that he always smiles his cheesy grin. He has shiny white teeth like milk and one gold one like a pirate would have, so when he smiles it's really sparkly and bright. It's the best trick to stop Michael from crying in the night, just to give him a superstar smile. It doesn't work as well when I do it though because when I smile really big my eyes go all squinty and
30 Daddy says I look more like someone has stood on my toe than someone who is feeling happy, so maybe I frighten Michael rather than cheering him up. Daddy is nearly always happy, except when he loses the car keys. Actually, I only ever saw him cry once, but he said it wasn't because he was sad - it was just because he had something sharp in his eye. I think he was a bit sad
35 though.

I will tell you the story. He didn't come to pick me up from school so I had to go home with Mrs Hewitt and I had cheese sandwiches for dinner. When it was really late and I was falling asleep on the sofa, Mrs Hewitt drove me home in the dark. When Daddy opened the door to our house she must have got
40 something in her eye too, because I saw that her eyes were a little shimmery and sad-looking. She gave Daddy a long hug and said something in his ear. He kept his eyes scrunched up tight and nodded and sniffed and then Mrs Hewitt gave me a squeeze on the hand and left.

When I looked at Daddy his eyes were sore-looking and all puffed up like how
45 mine look if I cry too much. This is what I said:

"What's wrong, Daddy? Have you been doing lots of work all night?"

And he said, "No, Bella," (He normally calls me Bella or Issy instead of Isabella.), "Come inside, we need to have a grown-up chat."

"Are you ill, Daddy?"

50 "No, love. I'm fine."

We went into the kitchen and he had hot chocolate with marshmallows ready for me and him on the table.

"Daddy, why are your eyes sore?"

"It's nothing, Bella. I have something sharp in my eye that hurts so my eyes
55 have been watering a bit."

"Oh, okay. Why did I have to go to Mrs Hewitt's house? And where's Mummy? I wanted to tell her-"

"Honey, I've got a few things to explain that are a little complicated, so I need you to listen quietly for a little while so that I can explain them in the best way
60 possible. Do you understand? Can you hold tight for just a minute?"

I remember that he was speaking very slowly and quietly and looking at me like how he looks at his computer screen at night.

"Yes, Daddy."

"Isabella..."

65 He didn't say anything for a bit so I waited. He was breathing very loudly.

"Daddy, are you alright?"

The sharp thing in his eye must have scratched him a little extra, because he started to cry again. I went over to give him a cuddle, and I felt the wet patch on the front of his t-shirt. He was shaking like he was cold, so I rubbed his arms
70 with my hands, trying to warm him up. It didn't really help, though. My hands are very small.

"Bella. Do you remember that Mummy had a baby growing inside her tummy and she was getting very big and round?"

"Yes, because the baby is nearly here!"

75 "Well, Bella, you're right. Mummy went into hospital today and...in fact, now you have a lovely, cute baby brother, who is going to love you very much."

"Oh, Daddy! Isn't that so good? I knew it would be a boy, I knew it! Where is he? Can I see?"

"He's still in the hospital, love. The doctors are keeping him there to make sure
80 he's nice and healthy and happy."

"Is Mummy there with him? When are they coming home?! Oh, Daddy, aren't you so happy?"

"Bella. Bella...your brother...we'll be going to see him tomorrow in the hospital. But your mum... she won't be coming back from the hospital."

85 "What do you mean?"

"Having your brother was very difficult for your mother. The doctors...they tried...they..."

He stopped again, and blew his nose.

"Honey, listen. Your mother's not with us anymore."

90 "But when will she come back?"

"She's not going to be coming back here."

"Why does she have to stay at the hospital?"

"She...Bella, she's gone on. She's not going to be with us on Earth anymore. Do you understand what I'm trying to say?"

95   He kept on taking tissues from the box on the table and wiping his eyes.

"Daddy, are you sad?"

I tried to give him a cheesy grin to cheer him up, but I already told you, I'm not very good at it.

"No, love, I'm not sad…not really. And you shouldn't be too sad either. I'm
100 going to be just fine, you wait and see. You might miss Mummy a lot, like me, but remember that your mother's in a better place now."

"Don't worry, Daddy, I know Mummy will want to come back to see us."

And that's the only time I've seen Daddy cry. I didn't understand what happened to Mummy then but now I do. My Mummy is dead. But it's okay,
105 because me and Michael have got Daddy, and he's got us.

1. Why is Isabella more mature than other children of her age?

- a. She is taller.
- b. She has an older brother.
- c. She has had to take care of her father.
- d. She has had to take care of her younger brother.
- e. She has had to take care of her mother.

2. 'Boys will be boys.' (lines 8-9)
   What is this sentence an example of?

- a. a saying
- b. a title
- c. a question
- d. advice
- e. an exclamation

3. Why does Isabella think her father knows 'little secrets' (lines 12-13)?

- a. He is like Dumbledore.
- b. He is old.
- c. He is very smart.
- d. He finds secrets whilst working on his computer.
- e. He makes them up.

4. What does Isabella think the typing on the keyboard sounds like?

- a. the pitter-patter of tiny feet
- b. hailstones falling on the ground
- c. a room full of fast typists
- d. numbers being punched into a calculator
- e. rain falling on a window

5. Why does Isabella think her father is 'nearly always happy' (line 32)?

- a. He has shiny, white teeth.
- b. He is always laughing.
- c. She has only seen him cry once.
- d. He has never cried.
- e. He never loses his car keys.

6. Why do you think Mrs Hewitt's eyes are 'a little shimmery' (line 40)?

    ⬭ a. They are a shimmery blue colour.

    ⬭ b. They were brimming with tears.

    ⬭ c. They were shining with excitement.

    ⬭ d. She was wearing contact lenses.

    ⬭ e. She had something in her eye.

7. Which of the following is the best synonym for the word 'scrunched' (line 42)?

    ⬭ a. relaxed

    ⬭ b. hunched

    ⬭ c. squashed

    ⬭ d. creased

    ⬭ e. baggy

8. 'He was breathing very loudly.' (line 65)
Why was Isabella's father breathing loudly?

    ⬭ a. He was feeling tired and out-of-breath.

    ⬭ b. He was feeling impatient and frustrated.

    ⬭ c. He was feeling scared and panicky.

    ⬭ d. He was feeling distressed and uncomfortable.

    ⬭ e. He was feeling angry and tense.

9. Why did Isabella's mother go into hospital?

    ⬭ a. She was giving birth.

    ⬭ b. She had fallen ill.

    ⬭ c. She had booked an appointment.

    ⬭ d. She needed an x-ray scan.

    ⬭ e. She was accompanying Isabella's father.

10. 'The doctors...they tried...they...' (lines 86-87)
Why did Isabella's father not finish his sentence?

    ⬭ a. Isabella interrupted him.

    ⬭ b. He needed to sneeze.

    ⬭ c. He forgot what he was saying.

    ⬭ d. Isabella began to cry.

    ⬭ e. He was overcome by grief.

11. Why did Isabella's father not say the words 'Your Mummy is dead.'?
- a. He was trying to find a sensitive way of explaining it to Isabella.
- b. He didn't want to lie to Isabella.
- c. Isabella would not understand this sentence.
- d. He didn't want Isabella to know.
- e. He was trying to make the conversation last as long as he could.

12. 'I know Mummy will want to come back to see us.' (line 102)
What does this sentence tell us about Isabella's understanding of the situation?
- a. She is optimistic.
- b. She has understood the situation very quickly.
- c. She doesn't think her father understands the situation.
- d. She does not understand what has happened.
- e. She is confused.

13. Why did Isabella's father call her 'love' (lines 50 and 79) and 'honey' (lines 58 and 89)?
- a. He was trying to cheer her up.
- b. They are Isabella's middle names.
- c. He was being restrained.
- d. He was trying to get her attention.
- e. He was being affectionate.

14. Why has the author used very simplistic language throughout the passage?
- a. The author has a small vocabulary.
- b. The passage is intended to be read by young children.
- c. The author is trying to mimic the voice of someone who is five-years old.
- d. The author does not want to confuse the reader.
- e. The passage is a simple story.

15. In what narrative is the passage written?
- a. 1st person without opinions
- b. 1st person with opinions
- c. 3rd person without opinions
- d. 3rd person with opinions
- e. a mixture of different narratives

Miss Fortune's Galley (Test 3)

Marking Grid															
Question	1	2	3	4	5	6	7	8	9	10	11	12	13	14	15	Total
✓ or ✘																

Read the following instructions carefully:

1. You have 12 minutes to complete this test of 15 questions.

2. You are recommended to spend 5 minutes reading the text, and 7 minutes answering the questions.

3. Work as quickly and as carefully as you can.

4. When you have finished a page, continue straight on to the next page. Do not waste time.

5. You can write on the text itself, or use the available space on the question paper to do any working. However, only mark your final answer in the answer boxes.

6. Mark your answer using a pencil, by drawing a firm horizontal line in the box next to your chosen option.

7. To change an answer, rub out your original answer completely and then mark on your new choice.

8. If you cannot answer a question, go on to the next question.

9. When you have completed the paper, use the time remaining to go back to any questions you have missed out and check your answers.

Good luck!

'Miss Fortune's Galley'

"AHOY thar, Fishbait, strike the colours while we're near t' land, would ye?" barked Suzy Smythe from the bow of Fortune's Galley, her salt-sprayed hair whipping and whirling in the sea breeze like scarlet tongues of fire.

"Aye, capt'n!" came a scratchy adolescent voice from behind her.

5　Suzy stood triumphant, feet placed squarely at shoulders' distance apart, surveying the ocean as a queen surveys her kingdom. It was a rare occasion, but on this day she had donned her full captain's kit, which included her most officious tricorn hat and a long, navy, billowing coat secured with a belt across the waist. Young Jack Linton admired her impressive silhouette as he darted up
10　the mast, took down the black and claret flag and slung it over his shoulder. When he returned, Suzy inhaled deeply and closed her eyes, listening to the sloshing of the ocean waves against her ship and smiling to herself.

"Mornin', bucko," said Suzy, sensing Jack's presence next to her. "I'n't she beautiful?"

15　"The sea, capt'n?"

"O' course, Fishbait! She's got spirit today. A sapphire sky, a blazin' sun and a jolly jumpin' sea. Now that's a good life."

"Well blow me down, Miss Suzy, yer a right merry wench this mornin'!"

"I'm always a merry wench, ye blaggard!" chuckled Suzy, slapping Jack so hard
20　on his back that he lurched forward, and had to grab Suzy's arm to steady himself. Once upright, he let go hastily, avoiding Suzy's eyes and attempting to dispel the colour rising in his face. He cleared his throat.

"I know why yer bones are all tingly, capt'n. Our last plunder were a good haul, weren't it? All thanks te yerself."

25　Suzy grinned toothily at him, displaying a kaleidoscope of white, gold, silver and brown.

"I'll tell ye a secret. Fortune's Galley is the richest girl upon the seven seas, and don't nobody even know it. Can't nobody come after us nor take the treasure back neither. We're as free as birds and we've got more gold, doubloons and finery than an Arab prince. Yes, boy, our last plunder were a *very* good haul, 'cause I'm a *very* good capt'n. Now, Fishbait, get yer scrawny bottom below deck and bring me up a large pint o'rum. Shout ahoy t' the crew on yer way as well, it's time we had a good jig!" Suzy sent him off with a wink and a shove, and poor young Jack scampered off, cheeks burning, turning back only once to catch a final glimpse of Suzy at the helm, resplendent in her joy.

Once Jack had successfully roused One-Eyed Nick from his mid-morning nap (by tipping him out of his hammock), fetched some barrels of their best rum and called Crabby Titchson and Anne Rackham from their cabins, he hunted down the troublesome trio of Mad George, Bonny Bess and Will de Sang, who were busy cleaning blood from their newly-inherited cutlasses and singing mindless ditties about pirates far poorer than them.

"Ahoy thar, me hearties! Belay that racket - the cap'n wants ye all at top deck," he bellowed over their raucousness. The singing gradually petered out as he gave them a hard look, at which point Will de Sang caught his eye, and called back, "Arghh, 'tis young Jack Linton! Lookie here, you go tell yer lass Suzy-"

"Oh stow that; don't be disrespectin' capt'n Suzy by implyin' she's a lass t' nobody, ye hear!" interjected Jack, his cheeks pinker than sunrise.

"Come on, Fishbait, we all know ye'd go bow-legged for our Suzy Smythe," sniggered Will.

"The cabin boy and the capt'n, whoever heard of such a tale?" added Bess.

"Enough w' yer bilge! Just drop yer swords and get yerselves up top, will ye?" he snapped in reply. The trio stood up to follow him, Will and Bess grinning broadly with amusement. Mad George sped up a little to walk alongside Jack, and said in an amicable voice, "S'alright, Jack; don't let the others make yer belly yellow. Yer a good lad and Suzy'll see ye as such. They're only rattlin' yer rudder."

Jack smiled weakly and nodded to George to thank him for his kindness, and they all went up as chums to celebrate with Suzy. The crew had a magnificent day; two barrels of golden rum they drained (even Jack had a bit), and they swayed arm-in-arm, singing sea shanties to the empty waves as the sun sank through the sky, surrounded by all the wealth they had acquired.

So wrapped up were they in their dances and their laughter, that they didn't notice the air getting colder and the mist descending around the white sails of Fortune's Galley. In fact, perhaps it was the rum, or perhaps it was due to the misfortune they had stumbled upon, they all began to feel very drowsy, so drowsy that one-by-one they lay their heads on the oaken deck and were snatched into sleep, unaware of the darkening sky and rumbling clouds. Even the sea turned from a choppy cerulean to a grim, deathly, unmoving black.

Time passed.

Suzy was the first to wake. Her eyes snapped open and swam, adjusting to the dim light. She was startled to find that she could not see further than three feet in front of her, as the fog hung thick and heavy in the air. Her skin prickled with cold, and she drew her coat desperately around her to retain what little body heat she had left. Suzy winced as she realised that they had all fallen asleep, with no-one steering the ship; they could have drifted anywhere, and without clear long-distance vision, there was no way of working out where they might be. Her heart raced, pounding with guilt and fear.

As she sat up, the rest of the crew began to come to their senses, all of them as confused as each other. No-one breathed a word - they all knew they were in trouble, and there was no need to voice that fact unless someone had a plan. Minutes ticked by in silence, until gradually and menacingly, a warbling cohort of male voices reached their ears, half-singing, half-screeching a familiar tune:

"Oh, poor old man, your horse will die,
And we say so, and we know so,
Oh, poor old man, your horse will die
Oh, poor old man!
We'll hoist him up to the main yardarm,
Say I, old man, your horse will die!
We'll drop him down to the depths of the sea
Say I, old man, your horse will die!"

As the crew listened, Jack hoisted himself upright and walked tentatively to the edge of the ship, planks creaking dissonantly under his boots. He peered out through the fog, eyes straining, ears filled with the haunting, tuneless song emanating from the misty ocean.

95 *"We'll sing him down with a long, long roll*
Where the sharks'll have his body
And the devil will have his soul!"

Crabby Titchson coughed, and muttered gruffly, "What in the name o' Davy Jones is happenin' here?"

100 "S'another ship out thar; listen," remarked Will.

"They're awful singers, by gum. 'S all out o' tune," said Anne, trembling.

"Argghh, they's only drunk sailors," said One-Eyed Nick dismissively, getting to his feet.

"Avast me hearties, I see summat; I see the ship!" exclaimed Jack, whose torso
105 was stretched out over the side of the deck as far as it would go.

"What is't? What's she called?" asked Nick.

Jack looked back at the crew, disbelief and terror etched upon his 16-year-old pockmarked face.

"Shiver me timbers... It's the Marie Celeste."

110 Suzy flinched started at Jack's words, eyes widening as the stern of the Marie Celeste drifted closer, now faintly visible through the fog. All could see the name, carved onto the side of the ship in bold, cursive script. And all knew it could not be good, as Suzy gulped and drew her cutlass from her belt.

"They ain't no drunken sailors like we be. They's like what we might be, if
115 we're not careful. I heard it said upon the seas too many times, that yer doom be at hand if ye ever see a ship by the name o' Marie Celeste, and hear voices singin' an old shanty. 'Cause only ghosts can't never sing in tune."

1. What colour is Suzy's hair?
   - a. black
   - b. blonde
   - c. brown
   - d. red
   - e. white

2. '...surveying the ocean as a queen surveys her kingdom.' (line 6)
   What literary technique is prevalent in this phrase?
   - a. personification
   - b. metaphor
   - c. simile
   - d. onomatopoeia
   - e. alliteration

3. Which of the following is part of Suzy's captain's outfit?
   - a. an eye-patch
   - b. a long, black coat
   - c. tights
   - d. a top hat
   - e. a belt

4. What time of day is it at the beginning of the story?
   - a. night
   - b. midday
   - c. evening
   - d. afternoon
   - e. morning

5. Why does Jack have colour 'rising in his face' (line 22)?
   - a. He is embarrassed that Suzy had managed to jolt him.
   - b. He is overheated.
   - c. He is angry at Suzy for hitting him.
   - d. He is about to be sick.
   - e. He is a chameleon.

6. Why do you think Suzy has a 'kaleidoscope of white, gold, silver and brown' (lines 25-26) in her mouth?

⬭ a. Some of her teeth are rotten or have been replaced with fake ones.
⬭ b. She has piercings in her mouth.
⬭ c. Some of her teeth have fallen out.
⬭ d. She has a multi-coloured sweets her mouth.
⬭ e. She is in the middle of eating.

7. How many crew members are there on Fortune's Galley?
⬭ a. two
⬭ b. three
⬭ c. five
⬭ d. eight
⬭ e. ten

8. What is Jack's position within the crew?
⬭ a. fishbait
⬭ b. cabin boy
⬭ c. captain
⬭ d. cook
⬭ e. first mate

9. Why do the other crew members tease Jack?
⬭ a. They dislike him.
⬭ b. He has a funny voice.
⬭ c. He is the youngest.
⬭ d. He likes Suzy.
⬭ e. He is weak.

10. How does the atmosphere change between lines 58 and 68?
⬭ a. It goes from sad to eerie.
⬭ b. It goes from happy to sad.
⬭ c. It goes from happy to eerie.
⬭ d. It goes from eerie to happy.
⬭ e. It goes from tense to relaxed.

11. Why don't the crew notice the changes in the weather?

⬭ a. The changes are very gradual.
⬭ b. They are too engrossed in celebrating.
⬭ c. They are too drunk.
⬭ d. They are blind.
⬭ e. A spell makes them unaware.

12. Why does Suzy draw her coat around her when she wakes up?

⬭ a. She is using her coat as a shield.
⬭ b. The rest of her clothes have disappeared.
⬭ c. She is scared.
⬭ d. She is hiding.
⬭ e. She is cold.

13. Which of the following best characterises the song the crew hear?

⬭ a. angelic
⬭ b. catchy
⬭ c. fun
⬭ d. chilling
⬭ e. a solo

14. According to Anne Rackham, what is unpleasant about the song?

⬭ a. It is sung by men.
⬭ b. It is about death.
⬭ c. It is sung by women.
⬭ d. It is boring.
⬭ e. It is sung out of tune.

15. To whom does Suzy believe the singing voices belong?

⬭ a. ghosts
⬭ b. the police
⬭ c. other pirates
⬭ d. drunken sailors
⬭ e. no one

Safety (Test 4)

Marking Grid															
Question	1	2	3	4	5	6	7	8	9	10	11	12	13	14	15	Total
✔ or ✘																

Read the following instructions carefully:

1. You have 12 minutes to complete this test of 15 questions.

2. You are recommended to spend 5 minutes reading the text, and 7 minutes answering the questions.

3. Work as quickly and as carefully as you can.

4. When you have finished a page, continue straight on to the next page. Do not waste time.

5. You can write on the text itself, or use the available space on the question paper to do any working. However, only mark your final answer in the answer boxes.

6. Mark your answer using a pencil, by drawing a firm horizontal line in the box next to your chosen option.

7. To change an answer, rub out your original answer completely and then mark on your new choice.

8. If you cannot answer a question, go on to the next question.

9. When you have completed the paper, use the time remaining to go back to any questions you have missed out and check your answers.

Good luck!

'Safety'

TOTO reached automatically for his mother's slender tail and found it reassuringly swishing exactly where it ought to be, just above his head, sweeping small, soothing showers of red, dry dust into the air so that they fell, gently landing, on top of his wrinkly head. He gladly wrapped the end of his
5 trunk around it and gripped tightly, giving a little triumphant tug. He instantly felt much better.

Letting out a dismissive sigh, Ife shook her head slowly, expelling a colossal wave of dust into the air and unintentionally disturbing a few flies who expressed their surprise and irritation with several disgruntled buzzes before
10 settling, indignantly, back onto her folded, grey skin. She had only wanted to play, but once again little Toto had run back to his mother, scampering as quickly as his big clumsy legs would allow him. Exasperated, Ife rolled her eyes and hauled her great body round, heading grudgingly back to the cool shade of the acacia tree.

15 The rest of the herd were spread across the bush, swaying sluggishly beneath the limited shade and drowsily munching on acacia leaves. Scanning the vast savannah, Ife moved her great head hopefully, searching for some sign of activity or any source of intrigue that she could explore; yet the heat was nearing its inexorable peak and the adults were slipping into idleness. Ife
20 released another sigh, bored and fed up with the unvarying schedule of inactivity, and resigned herself to tug despondently at the branches above her.

The large, round disc of the Sun was rising steadily in the sky, carving his passage overhead, unstoppable, and aiming unswervingly for the midday point, from where he could beat down ruthlessly on everything below,
25 providing no merciful shadows in which to hide from the intense, dry heat of an African summer. Despite the comfort Toto gleaned from his mother, the heat was becoming unbearable. He felt a little confused, not able to comprehend why the Sun felt it necessary to be so harsh and pitiless: perhaps he was lonely up in the sky with no herd to keep him company. Toto sighed
30 sadly, overwhelmed by his thoughts and the nonsensical world around him. He moved in closer to his mother, squeezing her tail a little tighter and closing his eyes, breathing in the warm familiar scent that enclosed him in a bubble of

safety. The regular rhythm of his mother's heavy breaths, permanent and resistant to the changing nature of the outside world, instantly dispelled his troubled thoughts of the bitter Sun; the great weight of her vast ribcage heaved faithfully up and down, providing Toto with an unwavering certainty amongst the chaos of the new, unknown and unexplored.

Toto felt a gentle pull along his mother's tail and, opening his eyes dazedly, began to plod along behind, unresisting and unquestioning, towards the welcome shade of the few trees left unoccupied that sparsely littered the bush. The big, round feet of his mother left firm, definite footprints in front of him, into which he placed his own smaller, perfect imitations. Kicking rough dust up into his sleepy eyes, she led him to the safe refuge of the trees where they could watch the afternoon drift languorously by.

In her peripheral vision, Ife caught sight of two of the more elderly members of the herd break into a panicked trot, flapping their immense ears as they sped across the savannah. She turned her head eagerly, anticipating the arrival of a gazelle or a giraffe, anything that might cause even a trivial drama to unfold that she could watch from the sympathetic shade of her tree. The dense, wavering air rippled just above the ground, making it difficult to make out clean shapes through the smoggy atmosphere: a handful of two-legged animals were darting between distant trees, holding metallic sticks in their hands and keeping low to the ground as they picked out a path that led decidedly towards the elephants' peaceful haven.

An uneasy sense of anxiety crept its way up Ife's trunk and nudged her importantly in the middle of her forehead; she gulped instinctively and it flowed, more confident now, down her throat, pouring into her stomach with an insistent splash that caused an unpleasant churning feeling. Unclear as to what these animals were, Ife took one assertive step with one great foot out of the meagre shade, squinting through the hazy air to satisfy her now more reluctant curiosity. An impertinent crack broke out from under her foot as a large, audacious branch gave way under her massive weight.

Suddenly, the two-legged animals crouched, searching frantically for the source of the sound, their metallic sticks poised and forward-pointing. One of them locked its eyes on Ife, on its face an unpleasant expression of focus and intent, mixed with something inexplicable that Ife had not encountered before:

malice. Alarmed, Ife dragged her great body round, stampeding back across the open bush and ploughing through the sparse greenery towards the rest of the herd as an unavoidable wave of panic surged up inside of her and drove her forwards like an unyielding tsunami.

Sharp cracks rang out behind her, each one sending a shockwave through the air that hit and reverberated off of every unsuspecting creature it found. The herd dispersed chaotically, blundering blindly in all directions, bewildered alarm evident in each pair of eyes and utter terror pounding through each and every heart.

Toto's tummy contracted violently as he felt his mother's rhythmic breathing break out of its persistent pattern, cutting the breath short for a brief moment before resuming again, much quicker than before. His mother lurched in front of him, blocking his view of the epicentre of the herd's dispersal. Heavy bangs and shouts now roared through the air as he was jostled forcefully out of the shade and into the exposed grassland; he picked up his feet, desperately hurrying mindlessly in the direction his mother was shoving him.

Frantically, he glanced up at his mother's face to find a wild look in her panic-stricken eyes where he had previously known only love and reassurance. All at once, she faltered, staggering forwards with an uncontrolled lunge, sending a cloud of angry, red dust high into the air, filling his eyes and forcing them to snap shut, stealing the view of his mother from him. Trumpeting with pain and fear, she stopped in her forward-moving tracks, thrashing her enormous head and trunk from side to side in an unseeing storm of anguish and stamping her huge feet angrily on the floor, leaving great scars of disorder on the once settled ground. Toto's ears rang, throbbing from the deafening scream and flapping with blind panic.

She tossed her head about with abandon, taking in the two-legged creatures now surrounding them, metallic sticks pointed forwards, some letting off bright sparks as they sent ear-splitting cracks reverberating into the dense, silent air. With her great feet she scooped Toto in underneath her, floundering wildly in all directions and throwing her massive weight behind each thrash of her heavy trunk as she lashed out desperately at the unforeseen threat. Overcome with terror and stumbling hopelessly under each intense impact that penetrated through her tough, dusty skin, she trumpeted belligerently at her attackers, desperately resolute on shielding Toto from their relentless assault.

A great crash and another explosion of hot dust spread through the air next to Toto, showering him with another barrage of debris and a fresh cascade of
105 alarm. His mother's great, majestic head hit the ground with a heavy thud, shaking her large ears and sending vibrations down her long trunk. Hearing incomprehensible noises closing in, Toto turned around and backed towards her, stumbling clumsily over her great legs that lay chaotically across the dishevelled floor of the bush. He felt something hard and slender beneath his
110 foot and, realising what it was, scrabbled on the floor with his trunk, wrapping it tightly round his mother's tail and giving a firm, reassuring squeeze, just to let her know that he was there to protect her.

1. '...sweeping small, soothing showers of red, dry dust...' (line 3)
   What literary technique is prevalent in this phrase?
   - ⬭ a. onomatopoeia
   - ⬭ b. a simile
   - ⬭ c. alliteration
   - ⬭ d. a metaphor
   - ⬭ e. repetition

2. Which of the following is the best synonym for the word 'exasperated' (line 12)?
   - ⬭ a. infuriated
   - ⬭ b. reassured
   - ⬭ c. pacified
   - ⬭ d. delighted
   - ⬭ e. relieved

3. What are the elephants doing with the acacia leaves?
   - ⬭ a. laying on them
   - ⬭ b. eating them
   - ⬭ c. standing on them
   - ⬭ d. smelling them
   - ⬭ e. playing with them

4. What reason does Toto suggest for the harshness of the Sun?
   - ⬭ a. The Sun is angry.
   - ⬭ b. The Sun is unhappy.
   - ⬭ c. The Sun enjoys being unfriendly.
   - ⬭ d. The Sun is lonely.
   - ⬭ e. The Sun doesn't like elephants.

5. Which of the following best describes Toto's mother's breathing in lines 33-36?
   - ⬭ a. irregular
   - ⬭ b. slow
   - ⬭ c. fast
   - ⬭ d. shallow
   - ⬭ e. reliable

6. Why does Ife turn her head eagerly in line 47?
   - ⬭ a. She wants to race the elderly members of the herd.
   - ⬭ b. She has heard a gazelle approaching.
   - ⬭ c. She is looking for more shade.
   - ⬭ d. She is looking for more acacia leaves.
   - ⬭ e. She hopes that something interesting is happening.

7. What type of word is 'anxiety' (line 55)?
   - ⬭ a. an adjective
   - ⬭ b. an adverb
   - ⬭ c. a noun
   - ⬭ d. a preposition
   - ⬭ e. a verb

8. Why did an 'impertinent crack' (line 61) break out?
   - ⬭ a. Ife broke a branch by stepping on it.
   - ⬭ b. Ife had pushed a tree over.
   - ⬭ c. Ife's ankle snapped.
   - ⬭ d. A thunderstorm had started.
   - ⬭ e. A firework had gone off.

9. Which of the following is the best definition for the word 'malice' (line 67)?
   - ⬭ a. a look of confusion
   - ⬭ b. a desire to succeed
   - ⬭ c. a desire to harm someone or something
   - ⬭ d. a type of head lice
   - ⬭ e. a type of injury

10. How might the members of the herd have been feeling as they 'dispersed chaotically' (line 73)?
   - ⬭ a. excited
   - ⬭ b. frightened
   - ⬭ c. calm
   - ⬭ d. furious
   - ⬭ e. indignant

11. 'His mother lurched in front of him, blocking his view...' (lines 78-79)
    In what tense is this sentence written?
    - a. future tense
    - b. present tense
    - c. future passive tense
    - d. past tense
    - e. a mixture of tenses

12. Why were Toto's eyes forced to 'snap shut' (line 87)?
    - a. The glare from the Sun was too bright.
    - b. He was scared of the sight in front of him.
    - c. His mother told him to close his eyes.
    - d. He didn't want to see his mother anymore.
    - e. His eyes were filled with dust.

13. What are the 'two-legged creatures' with 'metallic sticks' that are described in lines 93-96?
    - a. humans with guns
    - b. monkeys with guns
    - c. monkeys with whistles
    - d. humans with whistles
    - e. humans with spears

14. Why did vibrations travel down Toto's mother's trunk in line 106?
    - a. She had been given an electric shock.
    - b. She trumpeted very loudly.
    - c. There was an explosion nearby.
    - d. A cloud of dust tickled her trunk.
    - e. Her head had fallen to the ground.

15. What type of word is 'clumsily' (line 108)?
    - a. an adjective
    - b. a conjunction
    - c. a verb
    - d. a preposition
    - e. an adverb

Sub Umbra (Test 5)

Marking Grid															
Question	1	2	3	4	5	6	7	8	9	10	11	12	13	14	15	Total
✔ or ✘																

Read the following instructions carefully:

1. You have 12 minutes to complete this test of 15 questions.

2. You are recommended to spend 5 minutes reading the text, and 7 minutes answering the questions.

3. Work as quickly and as carefully as you can.

4. When you have finished a page, continue straight on to the next page. Do not waste time.

5. You can write on the text itself, or use the available space on the question paper to do any working. However, only mark your final answer in the answer boxes.

6. Mark your answer using a pencil, by drawing a firm horizontal line in the box next to your chosen option.

7. To change an answer, rub out your original answer completely and then mark on your new choice.

8. If you cannot answer a question, go on to the next question.

9. When you have completed the paper, use the time remaining to go back to any questions you have missed out and check your answers.

Good luck!

Once you have completed each test and marked it using the answers at the back you can anonymously go online and compare your child's performance relative to peers who have completed the same test(s) using our 11+ Peer Compare System™. Register at http://peercompare.elevenplusexams.co.uk/ and then activate the access code printed on the front inside cover of this book.

'Sub Umbra'

"MR Maguire, have you been briefed?" said Louis Brodeur, his delicate ivory hands fastening the clasp on a file marked 'UMBRA' as he raised a single eyebrow at the figure crossing the atrium. "The relevant information is contained within this file; please, take some time to read it before you step outside, as per the protocol."

At these words, Rafe Maguire paused, mid-step, and surveyed the skeletal albino man behind the reception desk. His face was not familiar; he was the new administrator. Rafe's green eyes twinkled wryly as he read the name plate on Louis' desk and he opened his mouth to respond:

"Monsieur Brodeur, mon ami," he said with impeccable Parisian diction, "As a recent addition to the staff here, I understand your desire to follow protocol. However, there is small...*quirk* essential to the way I work. I entered the agency at the age of twenty-two. I am now thirty-six. The first time I was forced to read a briefing packet was also the *last* time I was forced to read a briefing packet. For fourteen years I have not needed, nor *wanted* protocol. And nor will you, with anything concerning me. Besides," he took the file from Louis and flipped it over to expose its reverse, where a faint silhouette of a wolf had been stamped into the top right-hand corner, "there's no point in my reading this - I *made* the thing."

Louis was quite unfazed by Rafe's imperious monologue and continued about his paperwork without giving Rafe a second glance.

"Excellent, sir. I will leave it for the stand-by agents."

Rafe's lip curled, impressed by the new boy's apathy. The MI6 administrators were normally very unrelenting in their love of procedure. Free from such a chore, Rafe gave Louis an approving nod (which went unnoticed) and made his way to the glass double doors to the west of the atrium. They parted smartly, releasing him from the cool interior into the sweltering summer sun. Outside, he squinted through the blinding light, beads of sweat already forming under his raven locks. Oxygen filled his lungs. He could smell success upon the breeze.

The assignment required him to drive across the city. As he coasted through town in his shiny, new toy (a BMW 7 Series), Rafe turned the case over in his mind. Target: Anna Amine, fiancé of Shadow Lord Chancellor Grant Basington. Background of target: supposed expatriate from Moscow, duration of British

35 Residency so far unknown, identity unverified. Aims: to draw out any knowledge she may have of intelligence traders in the UK, to establish her position within this ring, should she be part of it, and to keep CIA cover intact to avoid alerting intelligence traders to MI6's knowledge of their activities. Cover details: CIA agent Michael Maguire, an old friend of Grant Basington.

40 After about half an hour Rafe arrived in suburbia, eventually recognising Basington's humble home from the satellite pictures, teardrops of merry wisteria adorning its sun-bleached brick walls. Rafe's monochrome attire was notably incongruous in this bright-pastel idyll, so he removed his suit jacket to reveal a crinkled white shirt. Rolling his sleeves up and unbuttoning somewhat,

45 he strolled up the empty driveway, and rang the bell. His body language was relaxed, as one should appear on a languid summer's afternoon, but his heart was hard and his pulse slightly elevated. The door swung open with the whisper of a creak.

"Hello, can I help you?"

50 Before him stood a breathtakingly beautiful woman of about 5'2", barely a shadow in comparison to Rafe's towering 6'3". She wore a paisley-patterned, blue summer dress that stopped just above her ankles, the material mostly obscured by cascading curls of long, brown hair, dense and glistening with moisture from a recent wash. Her face, distinctly Russian, had large

55 brown, feline-shaped eyes, rimmed elegantly with kohl, and, at this point in time, framed by a pair of neatly-shaped, inquisitive eyebrows.

Rafe gave her a stern look, briefly waving a silvery badge he drew from his pocket.

"Michael Maguire, CIA. I'd like to have a word with you Miss Amine, about

60 Shadow Lord Chancellor Grant Basington," he said, embellishing his American accent with a Chicago twang.

The woman's eyes widened at his words, her lips slightly parted in a voiceless 'Oh!' of surprise and confusion. Rafe then allowed his face to soften, and let out a cheery chuckle, slipping the badge back into his pocket.

65 "Sorry, didn't mean to scare you - that was just a little trick I rarely get to pull...It's fun to flash the badge, but I'm not really on duty right now, so you can relax. I just wanted to come and surprise Grant - I'm an old friend of his from university. You must be Anna, the famous fiancé," said Rafe, smiling broadly and shaking her hand enthusiastically.

70 "Yes, I'm Anna, though I would hardly call myself famous," replied the woman, laughing with relief, "Wow, you really gave me a fright!" Her accent, Rafe noted, was mostly anglicised, but she had a vague hint of a Russian-influenced pronunciation crept around the vowel sounds. She also had a curiously smooth tone of voice, low pitched for a woman, yet it caressed the ears as
75 pleasantly as silk on the skin.

"Are you really a CIA agent?"

Rafe tapped his nose. "Well yes - in fact, it was Grant's vote of confidence that got me the job. He's very well connected. I'm not meant to let you know, but as you're his fiancé...Is he at home?"

80 "I'm afraid he's not at the moment; he's gone into the city for a meeting."

"Oh, damn! I really should have called ahead, shouldn't I...it's just that I haven't seen him in what, must be over ten years now! And since I was on this side of the Atlantic, I thought I'd just hop on over for an afternoon. What time will he be home, do you think?"

85 "Well, in about an hour perhaps? If you'd like to wait for him I can offer you some water and fresh fruit, although unfortunately I can't do much about the company." She smiled at him, amber eyes creased at the edges and full of warmth.

Rafe thanked her profusely in his American persona, and followed her in as she
90 led him through the hallway to the shaded relief of the kitchen. Rafe took note of minor details in the house: pictures of Grant's family but none of Anna's, so

she must have moved in quite recently; no pairs of women's shoes by the door, but several of men's shoes; a mobile phone on the kitchen counter which could not be Anna's as she held one in her hand, so either Grant had forgotten his or they had a spare one; Anna's right hand pulling open a drawer and extracting -

He had noticed too late.

Rafe's head thrust sickeningly against the cupboard door as Anna drove her shoulder into his chest and thrust him backward with the strength and precision of a trained fighter. His reflexes, slightly dulled by the shock of the attack, were still as quick as fourteen years of experience should make them, and he managed to grab her left arm with firm fingers and twist it behind her back. However, Anna hooked one tiny foot around his leg and jabbed aggressively at the back of his knee, causing him to buckle forwards. Triumphant, she then placed her foot on his neck, the arch of her petite foot embracing his Adam's apple, pinning him to the cupboard once again, and twirling the knife warningly between her fingers. Rafe gagged, barely able to breathe, feeling the crushing pressure against his throat.

"I know you are not a CIA agent. I know you are not a friend of Grant. Your real name is Rafe Maguire, and you work for MI6. Tell me what you're doing here, honestly and quickly, do you understand me?" she said, pressing the blade against the side of his neck.

Her voice was honey, laced with poison.

1. What does the description 'ivory hands' (lines 1-2) imply about Louis Brodeur's hands?

- a. They are brittle and easily broken.
- b. They are very white.
- c. They look like elephant's tusks.
- d. They look like piano keys.
- e. They are very slender.

2. Which of the following is the best definition for the word 'protocol' (line 5)?

- a. the arrangement of a collection of objects according to a particular pattern
- b. the end of a race
- c. to collect and combine data
- d. a person who takes a long time to wake up in the morning
- e. the official set of rules that govern a particular situation

3. What is Louis Brodeur's job?

- a. administrator
- b. head of MI6
- c. secret agent
- d. French teacher
- e. chauffeur

4. Why are the words 'quirk' (line 12), 'last' (line 14), 'wanted' (line 15) and 'made' (line 19) printed in italics?

- a. Rafe whispered them.
- b. They are ironic.
- c. Rafe said them with emphasis.
- d. They were spoken in a Parisian accent.
- e. They are quotations.

5. Which of the following best describes Louis' reaction to Rafe's speech?

- a. indifferent
- b. shocked
- c. embarrassed
- d. scared
- e. irritated

6. 'He could smell success upon the breeze.' (lines 29-30)
   How does this sentence imply Rafe is feeling?
   - a. impatient
   - b. hopeless
   - c. distracted
   - d. optimistic
   - e. relaxed

7. What was Rafe doing as he drove through town?
   - a. listening to the radio
   - b. thinking about the case
   - c. thinking about what he was going to eat for lunch
   - d. trying to read a map
   - e. turning a suitcase over on the seat next to him

8. Who does Rafe pretend to be?
   - a. Louis Brodeur
   - b. Grant Basington
   - c. Anna Amine
   - d. Rafe Maguire
   - e. Michael Maguire

9. Which of the following is the best antonym for the word 'monochrome' (line 42)?
   - a. greyscale
   - b. colourful
   - c. monotonous
   - d. dark
   - e. chromatic

10. Why was some of the material of Anna's dress not visible?
    - a. Her hair was covering it.
    - b. The doorway was dark.
    - c. She only poked her head out around the front door.
    - d. She was wearing an apron.
    - e. A long, black scarf was draped around her neck.

11. What literary technique is prevalent in the phrase 'cheery chuckle' (line 64)?

    ◯ a. repetition

    ◯ b. a simile

    ◯ c. alliteration

    ◯ d. onomatopoeia

    ◯ e. a metaphor

12. Which of the following best describes Anna's accent?

    ◯ a. American

    ◯ b. English

    ◯ c. Chicagoan

    ◯ d. French

    ◯ e. Russian

13. What reason did Rafe give for visiting the house?

    ◯ a. He wanted to get some information from Anna.

    ◯ b. He wanted to ask Grant

    ◯ to get him a job.

    ◯ c. He wanted to visit Grant Basington.

    ◯ d. He wanted to meet Anna as she was famous.

14. What type of word is 'against' (line 98)?

    ◯ a. a noun

    ◯ b. a preposition

    ◯ c. an adverb

    ◯ d. an adjective

    ◯ e. a verb

15. From what genre of book is this passage likely to come?

    ◯ a. fantasy

    ◯ b. science fiction

    ◯ c. humour

    ◯ d. mystery

    ◯ e. classical

The Great Wave (Test 6)

Marking Grid															
Question	1	2	3	4	5	6	7	8	9	10	11	12	13	14	15	Total
✔ or ✘																

Read the following instructions carefully:

1. You have 12 minutes to complete this test of 15 questions.

2. You are recommended to spend 5 minutes reading the text, and 7 minutes answering the questions.

3. Work as quickly and as carefully as you can.

4. When you have finished a page, continue straight on to the next page. Do not waste time.

5. You can write on the text itself, or use the available space on the question paper to do any working. However, only mark your final answer in the answer boxes.

6. Mark your answer using a pencil, by drawing a firm horizontal line in the box next to your chosen option.

7. To change an answer, rub out your original answer completely and then mark on your new choice.

8. If you cannot answer a question, go on to the next question.

9. When you have completed the paper, use the time remaining to go back to any questions you have missed out and check your answers.

Good luck!

Once you have completed each test and marked it using the answers at the back you can anonymously go online and compare your child's performance relative to peers who have completed the same test(s) using our 11+ Peer Compare System™. Register at http://peercompare.elevenplusexams.co.uk/ and then activate the access code printed on the front inside cover of this book.

'The Great Wave'

THE wave wept with the sea, recoiling under the empty gaze of the night. Ghosts of stars giggled, watching as he trembled with the wind and whispered a prayer to the moon, which hung, watery and calm, at the crest of the cloudless sky. He inhaled, mustering the very last dregs of his power, and
5   breathed out a dejected sigh, a paltry "Oosh…" which rolled out over the rocky shores. Nearby, a trio of fish skittered about the reef, babbling cruelly.

"They say he's the last of the greats."

"Shame."

"Terrible shame."

10 At every disdainful word the wave's great belly churned with embarrassment, but he did not roar; the sea was calm that night.

Further on, the land held its breath as small feet pattered across it, accompanied by the occasional drop of salty water. The little boy ran and choked out tears, gasping for breath, tanned skin bathing in the moonlight and
15 tingling with cold. Feeling his own loud, rugged heartbeat rattle his bones, he scrambled onto a large dry rock. He glanced at the ocean. And he didn't think. He just jumped.

The boy tumbled through the water, eyes wide, and the wave caught him in one gentle hand. He then laughed, a fierce array of bubbles exploding from his
20 mouth. All he could hear was the gentle slosh of the water as it folded in on itself, over and over again. He appreciated its soft ripple; it did not lash out at the rocks, or rise up to the stars, but just lay, shimmering with a melancholy beauty.

"The water…it's so beautiful," thought the boy.

25 "Thank you, young one. It's been a while since I have been called beautiful," replied the wave. The sound came as a gravelly rumbling.

"Who…who was that?" the boy thought, swirling around in alarm.

"What are you?" said the wave.

30 The boy, suddenly aware that he was not breathing, flailed his way to the water's surface and gasped as he gulped down the crisp night air. Wind rushed past his ears again.

"Hello?"

But there was no reply.

35 Understanding, the boy dived back down, this time vigilant for any sign of a person, any shadow of any creature. To his dismay, he saw only a cloudy black-blue that stretched on through a vast expanse of water.

"Is anyone here?" he thought to himself.

"Yes?" said the wave, chuckling.

"Who is that?"

40 "You haven't answered my question. What are you?"

"My name is Aiden. I am…human. Are you?"

"No. I am the wave. The Great Wave."

There was a pause as Aiden wrapped his head around those words. The Great Wave.

45 "I need breath."

And Aiden swam gracefully to the surface and let the breeze inflate his lungs. He felt a sense of fear tug at his mind, begging him to swim to the shore and run away. But his curiosity weighed him down, and back he sank, blinking into the darkness.

50 "Where are you?"

Again the wave sniggered. "I am everywhere, of course! I am a wave!"

Aiden dragged a hand through the water, enjoying the feeling of it sliding through the gaps in his fingers.

"Ow; that hurt!" grumbled the wave.

55 "Fight me off then!" grinned Aiden, now treading water and swinging his arms around with a gurgling laugh. Then, all at once, the water turned cold. Aiden stopped, a sad confusion plastered over his face.

"What happened?" he thought, drawing his knees towards him for warmth.

"The water imitated my mood. It turns cold when I am sad," mumbled the
60 wave.

"Why are you sad, then?"

"I cannot fight you off."

"Of course you can! You're a wave!"

The water rippled again, but this time with a grinding sadness.

65 "I *know* I am a wave! But I am weak! Have you ever seen the water splash against the rocks? Have you ever encountered a storm on this part of the land? I think not. I cannot. I am a wave, the last of the greats. But I am not great. I am weak. You do not understand."

Aiden went for air again, but returned with his heart full of sympathy.

70 "Wave, listen. Did you know I was sad, incredibly sad, just before I came here?"

"No...why were *you* sad?" whispered the wave, incredulous.

"Because in truth, I am also weak. My father is great and strong and tall. I am small. I was crying because the other children wouldn't let me chop the wood.
75 They said I was just a baby. But I have made a decision - I may not be great or strong or tall now, but I will train and I will grow. I will show them they were wrong, and I will be great. You will be great too! Just have faith, O Wave."

The wave could do nothing in return for this wisdom but play and dance joyfully with the boy. Suddenly, he felt strong. As the sun rose and cast a rose-
80 bud glow over the sea, Aiden told the wave he must return to the land. Flocks of birds skimmed the pink sky, disappearing from time to time behind white, fluffy clouds. Golden rays beat down on the beach, and the water rippled with more life and energy than ever before.

"I'll come back soon," said Aiden, calling to the sea from the sun-bleached pebbles. The wave, perhaps a little hurt, swept him away with a swish like a friendly hug, and hummed a song with the birds, full of cheer.

He did not even notice the babbling of the fish, until they drifted towards the shore.

"Yes, I saw him, wasting his time with that human."

"What a child. He *thinks* he is a great now."

The wave was listening. The sea was dangerously still, but the fish, oblivious to this, carried on.

"Pah, he thinks. He's a weakling."

"Pathetic."

"I AM NOT WEAK!" roared the wave, the humid air parting to make way for the rising beast, climbing to a great height, frothing white with anger. The fish held their breath. But, alas, he only curled gracefully back into the sea, and the beach resumed its weary slumber. The fish laughed.

"Ohhh, I am just terrified."

"I'm shaking in my scales!"

This was enough. The wave began to pour out angry tears. He swelled and rose at a steady pace, starting to flow over the shingle and moisten the dry cliffs. The sky cried with him, beginning at first with a slow, sad trickle, and then building up till the rain was positively torrential. The wave lapped it up, writhing in agony as he rose like a raging beast, frothing white at the mouth. The fish struggled against the current, turning over and over as the water swirled around in a mad panic, all following the wave as it pressed forwards ravenously, digesting the earth with every bit of hatred it had ever felt.

He was a thunderous storm, a wild, leaping tsunami. And he screamed into the distance: "I AM THE WAVE! I AM THE GREATEST OF THE GREATS! AND I SHALL BE POWERFUL!"

1. What impression is given of the personality of the wave in the opening description?
- a. He seems to have a bad temper.
- b. He seems jolly.
- c. He seems nasty.
- d. He seems to be depressed.
- e. He seems arrogant.

2. What sort of atmosphere is created by the setting of the story?
- a. eerie and melancholy
- b. warm and inviting
- c. awkward and uncomfortable
- d. full of excitement
- e. peaceful and content

3. What is it about the boy's behaviour that indicates he is upset about something?
- a. He is clenching his fists.
- b. His bones are rattling.
- c. He is running.
- d. He jumps in the water.
- e. He is crying.

4. What causes the boy to swim back to the surface soon after jumping into the sea?
- a. The voice he hears scares him.
- b. He can't breathe under the water.
- c. He sees a shark.
- d. He hears his mum calling him home.
- e. He is too cold underwater.

5. 'Understanding, the boy dived back down...' (line 34)
   What does he understand at this point?
- a. He is weak.
- b. The voice was not real.
- c. The voice came from under the water.
- d. He needs sleep.
- e. He is being tricked.

6. 'He felt a sense of fear tug at his mind, begging him to swim to the shore and run away.' (lines 47-48)
   Why doesn't the boy do this?
   - a. The shore is too far away to swim to.
   - b. He doesn't remember the way home.
   - c. The wave won't let him go.
   - d. He is too intrigued by the wave to leave.
   - e. He passes out before he can swim away.

7. How does the boy try to keep warm when the sea turns cold?
   - a. He rubs his hands together.
   - b. He treads water.
   - c. He tucks his knees up.
   - d. He hugs himself.
   - e. He lights a fire.

8. What was it that caused the boy to run to the beach, crying?
   - a. He was upset because of the weather.
   - b. His father hit him.
   - c. He hurt himself.
   - d. The fish had said mean things about him.
   - e. He was not permitted to help chop the wood.

9. How has the mood changed by dawn in comparison to the opening of the story?
   - a. It is happier.
   - b. It is sadder.
   - c. It is tenser.
   - d. It is more threatening.
   - e. It is more subdued.

10. What finally causes the wave to snap and lash out in anger?
   - a. the boy's leaving
   - b. the fish's jeering
   - c. the birds' flocking around the clouds
   - d. the light of dawn
   - e. his father's reprimanding him

11. Select the option that best characterises the phrase 'ghosts of stars' (line 2)?
- a. comedy
- b. satire
- c. a simile
- d. a metaphor
- e. a mistake

12. '...watery and calm, at the crest of the cloudless sky' (lines 3-4)
What literary technique is prevalent in this phrase?
- a. simile
- b. metaphor
- c. personification
- d. rhyme
- e. alliteration

13. What type of words are these?

'suddenly' 'but' 'and' 'as'

- a. conjunctions
- b. adjectives
- c. pronouns
- d. adverbs
- e. verbs

14. What is the rough time frame of this story?
- a. a year
- b. a week
- c. twenty-four hours
- d. a night
- e. an hour

15. What literary technique is used throughout the story for the characterisation of the wave, the fish and the other non-human characters?
- a. exaggeration
- b. rhyme
- c. imagery of smells
- d. dehumanisation
- e. personification

FIRST PAST THE POST®

The Train to the Platform (Test 7)

Marking Grid																
Question	1	2	3	4	5	6	7	8	9	10	11	12	13	14	15	Total
✓ or ✗																

Read the following instructions carefully:

1. You have 12 minutes to complete this test of 15 questions.

2. You are recommended to spend 5 minutes reading the text, and 7 minutes answering the questions.

3. Work as quickly and as carefully as you can.

4. When you have finished a page, continue straight on to the next page. Do not waste time.

5. You can write on the text itself, or use the available space on the question paper to do any working. However, only mark your final answer in the answer boxes.

6. Mark your answer using a pencil, by drawing a firm horizontal line in the box next to your chosen option.

7. To change an answer, rub out your original answer completely and then mark on your new choice.

8. If you cannot answer a question, go on to the next question.

9. When you have completed the paper, use the time remaining to go back to any questions you have missed out and check your answers.

Good luck!

Once you have completed each test and marked it using the answers at the back you can anonymously go online and compare your child's performance relative to peers who have completed the same test(s) using our 11+ Peer Compare System™. Register at http://peercompare.elevenplusexams.co.uk/ and then activate the access code printed on the front inside cover of this book.

'The Train to the Platform'

A GIRL hurried along a dark road in the middle of London, her damp shoes slapping down loudly on the wet floor and echoing through the deserted street. Her frozen hands were tucked deep into the pockets of a big, heavy jumper and her brown, frizzy hair, which usually framed her pale face, was

5 plastered to her neck; the rain fell around her, invisible except for beneath the few street lights that were bathing the empty pavement in an eerie glow. She kept her face down, away from the fierce rain, bitterly aware of the warmth escaping from her body with every breath. She watched it turn into steam and run eagerly away from her, seeking a warmer place to hide as she grew

10 steadily colder.

She hastened down the steps to the train station, gripping the hand rail tightly for fear of slipping down into the darkness. The sign above her, displaying the name of the station, was only half lit and buzzing as if the electricity, too, was restless and itching for a warmer place to rest.

15 The girl sat down heavily beneath a light on the platform and resigned herself to wait for the last train of the night. She heard a small, suppressed cough from the nearby bench and whipped her head around, alarmed at the first human sound that she had heard for the last few hours. Sitting on the bench was a middle-aged woman; well-dressed in a tight-fitting, black suit with shiny, black

20 high heels. Her hair was blonde, layered and cut short in a sensible, yet attractive hairstyle; at her feet sat a large, black bag, somewhat like Mary Poppins' carpet bag yet a little more sophisticated. The light above her flickered rudely in the silence and she glared up at it with a reproving stare; it went out with a pop.

25 Dejectedly, the girl returned to her own thoughts as she fiddled absent-mindedly with the hem of her overly large woollen jumper, dismissing the stranger on the platform who was to be her unwilling travelling companion for the evening. The distant remnant of a sound floated down from the world above, sharply breaking the silence; indignant barking was abruptly followed

30 by a somewhat irritated voice calling a name. The platform began to vibrate with a sense of self-importance as the train flew, exultant, through the tunnel, resolutely interrupting the far-off dialogue. With a triumphant ping the light

above the other woman burst back to life as abruptly as it had gone out, revealing an unexpectedly empty bench beneath it. The girl had not heard her leave. She had not heard a sound from her since the light above had puffed its final sigh and resigned, without warning, for the night.

The 'Please mind the gap!' announcement blared assuredly along the platform, wrenching her away from her disconcerting thoughts. She boarded the train, gladly sitting down on the dry, cushioned seats. The doors slid shut with a smug 'swish' and the train gleefully picked up speed to hurtle purposefully once more into the blackness.

The door at the end of the carriage flew open and the warm air inside the carriage was sucked grudgingly out into the tunnel, torn away from its comforting refuge. An unfriendly roaring burst through the carriage, accompanied by the reluctant travelling companion as she clambered through the opening, pausing an instant as she glanced down at the ground shooting past beneath her; she winced. She forced the door shut behind her, wrestling with it for a brief moment before adamantly cutting off the relentless protestations of the cold night air as it desperately tried to squeeze aboard the warm train that was careering unswervingly along its familiar path. She breathed a sigh of relief, hastily pushing her hair back into its place; making a concerted effort to recover her composure, she sat down and began searching through her big, black bag. Presently, a neatly folded newspaper was calmly produced and she proceeded to scan through its contents. The girl returned to gazing despondently through the window, beyond her uninteresting reflection and out into the darkness of the tunnel; the walls were flying past, black and indistinguishable except for the odd patch of graffiti and the grimy wiring that ran, neglected, along the inside of the passage. The sleepers on the railway track were faithfully drumming out their unmistakeable beat for the last time that day.

The carriage seemed deathly quiet. The girl was unable to detect even her own humdrum breathing.

"Surely, five minutes had passed since the train had left the station, yet not a single sound had been made save the train's persistent thrumming; the pages

65 of the woman's newspaper had not been turned once," the girl thought, stealing a quick look at her. "Yes, she appeared still to be reading." Feeling particularly bold as her intrigue and suspicions began to prevail against her more sound and judicious thoughts, she snuck another brief glance, just in time to catch the woman's eyes darting sheepishly back to her newspaper.

70 The girl smiled. It was an amused smile that crept across her face slowly but assertively, despite the girl's half-hearted attempt to quell its steady progress. She looked down at her hands, still distractedly toying with the edge of her knitted jumper.

Very shortly, the girl became acutely aware of being watched; she spun her
75 head round and met the woman's eye contact. An intense stare came from a pair of piercing green, crystal clear eyes; the girl blinked and broke away, returning once more to gaze through the cold window.

*

The train slowed down glumly, losing all of its wonderful momentum in just a few seconds; sulkily, it hissed to a halt at the empty station and the doors
80 swished open, rather less smugly than before. At the end of the carriage a newspaper was carefully folded and placed prudently into a big, black bag. A pair of shiny, black high heels belonging to a well-dressed woman alighted neatly from the train. With a weary yawn the doors to the train slid shut again and it reluctantly began to pick up speed as it prepared to lug itself into the
85 blackness one last time. A head with a sensible, yet attractive hairstyle turned round to watch it disappear and, with a pair of piercingly green eyes, caught sight of a pale face peering through the window, framed by brown, frizzy hair. The two pairs of eyes met for a fleeting second; the lady blinked and broke away, turning to the stairs leading out to the rainy world above. She fumbled
90 around in her bag whilst the distant sound of a dog barking from the street above could be heard, abruptly followed by an angry voice calling its name. A black umbrella was produced rimmed with a fine white line; the shiny, black high heels mounted the stairs out of the station, she gripped the hand rail tightly for fear of slipping back down into the darkness. The woman hurried
95 along the dark street on the outskirts of London, her damp shoes slapping down loudly on the wet floor and echoing through the deserted street.

1. Why was the girl's hair 'plastered to her neck' (line 5)?
- a. She had used a lot of hairspray.
- b. She hadn't washed it in a month.
- c. It was wet because she had just had a shower.
- d. It was very wet because of the rain.
- e. It was frizzy.

2. Which of the following best describes the atmosphere created in the opening paragraph?
- a. idyllic
- b. gloomy
- c. relaxed
- d. tense
- e. light-hearted

3. Why did the girl grip the hand rail tightly?
- a. She did not want to slip.
- b. She was afraid of the dark.
- c. Her hands were cold.
- d. She was running very fast.
- e. She found walking down stairs difficult.

4. Which of the following is the best synonym for the word 'restless' (line 14)?
- a. peaceful
- b. content
- c. frustrated
- d. tired
- e. agitated

5. Why was the girl 'alarmed' (line 17)?
- a. She saw something move.
- b. The light went out.
- c. She heard an unexpected cough from nearby.
- d. She heard someone speak.
- e. The platform started to shake.

6. '...a large, black bag, somewhat like Mary Poppins' carpet bag...' (lines 21-22)
   What type of phrase is this?

   ⬭ a. onomatopoeic
   ⬭ b. a title
   ⬭ c. a metaphor
   ⬭ d. a question
   ⬭ e. a simile

7. What does it mean when it says that the woman looked at the light 'with a reproving stare' (line 23)?

   ⬭ a. She was scared of the light.
   ⬭ b. She looked at it as if she wanted to tell it off.
   ⬭ c. Her eyes began to water.
   ⬭ d. She looked at it as if she was pleased with it.
   ⬭ e. She was grateful.

8. What type of word is 'pop' (line 24)?

   ⬭ a. onomatopoeia
   ⬭ b. adjective
   ⬭ c. verb
   ⬭ d. antonym
   ⬭ e. conjunction

9. 'The doors slid shut with a smug "swish" and the train gleefully picked up speed to hurtle purposefully once more into the blackness.' (line 39-41)
   What is this sentence an example of?

   ⬭ a. an instruction
   ⬭ b. a simile
   ⬭ c. alliteration
   ⬭ d. personification
   ⬭ e. a plot twist

10. Why did the woman wince as she entered the carriage?

   ⬭ a. She was imagining getting stuck in the doorway.
   ⬭ b. She had just eaten something very sour.
   ⬭ c. She was imagining falling beneath the train.
   ⬭ d. She was imagining shutting her finger in the door.
   ⬭ e. She didn't like the smell of the carriage.

11. What type of word is 'humdrum' (line 62)?
- a. a noun
- b. a verb
- c. a conjunction
- d. an adjective
- e. an adverb

12. Why did the girl sneak 'another brief glance' (line 68)?
- a. She suspected that the woman wasn't really reading.
- b. She wanted to see which newspaper the woman was reading.
- c. She was bored.
- d. She dared herself to.
- e. She thought the woman might tell her off.

13. Which of the following is the best antonym for the word 'quell' (line 71)?
- a. quench
- b. finish
- c. end
- d. laugh
- e. encourage

14. Which of the following is the best definition for the word 'alighted' (line 82)?
- a. set fire to
- b. jump lightly and gracefully
- c. descend from a train or other form of transport
- d. smile to oneself
- e. walk confidently whilst rolling one's hips

15. Which of the following are described in the last paragraph?
1. the train leaving the platform
2. a street in central London
3. a dog misbehaving
4. the girl leaving the station
- a. 1 and 2
- b. 1 and 3
- c. 1 and 4
- d. 3 and 2
- e. 3 and 4

BLANK PAGE

Thursday Night at Scott's (Test 8)

Marking Grid															
Question	1	2	3	4	5	6	7	8	9	10	11	12	13	14	15	Total
✓ or ✗																

Read the following instructions carefully:

1. You have 12 minutes to complete this test of 15 questions.

2. You are recommended to spend 5 minutes reading the text, and 7 minutes answering the questions.

3. Work as quickly and as carefully as you can.

4. When you have finished a page, continue straight on to the next page. Do not waste time.

5. You can write on the text itself, or use the available space on the question paper to do any working. However, only mark your final answer in the answer boxes.

6. Mark your answer using a pencil, by drawing a firm horizontal line in the box next to your chosen option.

7. To change an answer, rub out your original answer completely and then mark on your new choice.

8. If you cannot answer a question, go on to the next question.

9. When you have completed the paper, use the time remaining to go back to any questions you have missed out and check your answers.

Good luck!

Once you have completed each test and marked it using the answers at the back you can anonymously go online and compare your child's performance relative to peers who have completed the same test(s) using our 11+ Peer Compare System™. Register at http://peercompare.elevenplusexams.co.uk/ and then activate the access code printed on the front inside cover of this book.

'Thursday Night at Scott's'

THE door swung shut, allowing only a breath of crisp February air to sweep in, clinging to a harried-looking man swathed in dark knitted wool. His frail hands quaked with the might of the cold as he made his way through the dimly-lit corridor, ears pricked at the sound of hushed voices and a distant double bass. Nodding his head to the burly man at the end of the narrow hall, he pressed against heavy mahogany doors and his eyes fell upon a familiar scene. The room was dark and smoky, a smatter of people spread across it, each individually lounging in a chair, or else tapping their fingers to the sound of jazz.

It was late; the room would surely have been full an hour before, but left were the only remains of an eager crowd. Trevor Scott inhaled, allowing the smell of his very own jazz club to envelope him, entirely giddy with content. Only one thing was out of place in this room. Directly opposite the stage, a man was seated in the shadow of the back wall. Even in the half-light, one could see he was plainly not interested in his surroundings, but wholly absorbed in something else. This something that was so distracting Trevor could not see, as the man was placed just so that Trevor could only see his behind. The stranger wore red braces and charcoal slacks, as was conventional, and a mess of hair hung from his bowed head that shone a gold worthy of autumn. In such a relaxed atmosphere he was the only one who managed to create a sense of tension, his body crumpled over the empty dinner table. Trevor frowned, but declined to let this anomaly ruin his good mood. He ambled over to the table, putting on a slight, hopefully rather intimidating, swagger.

There was the swish of an opening door and Trevor heard the last, lingering notes of a mellow tune get snatched up by the raging wind outside. A petite, shivering figure skidded into the room, causing some men to disengage themselves from their *'Times'* crosswords and look around the room in alarm. The figure, whom Trevor had now established was a girl of teenage years, paused for a mere fraction of a second before hurling herself past the bemused guests and collapsing into a chair at the strange young man's table. Trevor, perplexed, crept closer.

The girl was huffing and puffing. Her berry-red face was framed by curls of a deep chestnut brown, and she was staring at the man with childlike fascination. To his dismay, Trevor was still unable to see what the man was doing.

"You're not my uncle," the girl said.

"I should hope not," the man replied, not looking up.

"I thought you were my uncle!"

The man made no reply.

40 "'Cause, you see, he rang the other day and said he would meet me here, and would be wearing red braces and grey slacks, and would sit at the back. But then I was late because of those blasted trains and couldn't find my way here, and it's just freezing outside – Nice painting by the way – so I was all in a flurry…" She stopped. The man had stood up abruptly, and began packing his

45 things into a briefcase. Trevor caught a glimpse of a small A5 canvas decorated with a rich purple and various blue hues, before the man put it away and began to speak:

"It was lovely meeting you, but it is quite plain that I am not your uncle, and I really must go."

50 "Well, that was rude," she muttered, turning up her nose at him.

"Oh, my mistake, is it important to you to run around harassing strangers? I'm so sorry to inconvenience you. Perhaps you would like me to humour you?" he said, dropping his briefcase back on the table. Trevor flinched as the table rocked, its worn, spindly legs struggling under the weight. The man held out a

55 hand and bent his six-foot body into a mock bow.

"Wilson Henry-Smith Danforth, thirty-four. Charmed." The girl's face, having now calmed to a more natural shade, smirked. She mock-curtsied in return, shaking his hand.

"Jane Abbot. Sorry; I only have two names. Oh, and I would prefer not to
60 divulge my age, especially to strange men like you."

"Yet you bore us with your life's troubles." He turned to go, sweeping up his briefcase and slinging his jacket over one shoulder. There was a moment when he caught sight of Trevor and he faltered a little, avoiding Trevor's embarrassed eyes.

65 "You're incredibly unhelpful," the girl said haughtily. "I don't know what I did that was so awful."

It was peculiar, Trevor thought - The anger slid off Wilson Henry-Smith Danforth's face and he set his things down on the table again. His body

language changed completely. A slender hand trembled its way through his
70 hair and he twisted his thin lips into an apologetic smile.

"You know what, you're right. I'm so sorry – I've had a perfectly awful day at
work and I'm tired and it's late – I know it's not much of an excuse, and I have
no right to be so rude to a sweet little girl like you, but I'm sorry." His voice had
suddenly become a lot lighter, friendlier. Trevor, who had really begun to
75 dislike this Wilson character, suddenly felt a surge of pity for him. Who didn't
get snappy when they were feeling down?

Jane Abbott's lips were pursed, giving Wilson an appraising look. She eyed
Wilson's hands as they twisted and knotted about each other. There was a
strange, awkward silence as the jazz tinkled on behind them and Wilson
80 hesitated to move, balanced precariously on one foot.

"Perhaps... I could help you find your uncle?" he spluttered, cocking an eager
right eyebrow. "It's late for a girl of your age to be wandering alone."

"All right, then. I suppose I could forgive you..." she said, smiling. "But I don't
trust you."

85 Wilson laughed a velvety melody, and retrieved his belongings, turning to
follow Jane out of the club. Right behind them was a very confused Trevor.
Wilson merely nodded, grinning broadly.

"Is that you, Mr Scott? Delightful show this evening. Best jazz in town," he said.

Trevor smiled almost unconsciously and the door swung shut behind the odd
90 pair, just a few wisps of smoke clinging to their retreating backs. He relaxed
into a more proverbial posture and his eyes swept across a familiar scene. The
room was dark and smoky, a smatter of people spread across it, each
individually lounging in a chair, or else tapping their fingers to the sound of
jazz.

95 "Nice man, that Wilson," Trevor muttered to the vacated dinner table, allowing
the smell of his very own jazz club to consume him, entirely giddy with
content, and the memory of another brief encounter already fading from his
mind.

But he didn't notice the winking, green light coming from the underside of
100 Wilson's table.

1. During which season does this story take place?

   ⬭ a. winter
   ⬭ b. spring
   ⬭ c. summer
   ⬭ d. autumn
   ⬭ e. monsoon

2. Who is Trevor?

   ⬭ a. a bouncer
   ⬭ b. a visitor to the jazz club
   ⬭ c. the owner of the jazz club
   ⬭ d. Jane Abbott's uncle
   ⬭ e. a musician

3. What is it about the stranger in the club that makes him seem out of place to Trevor?

   ⬭ a. He is wearing charcoal slacks.
   ⬭ b. He is wearing red braces.
   ⬭ c. He has blond hair.
   ⬭ d. He is sitting opposite the stage.
   ⬭ e. He seems tense.

4. Why does the girl think this stranger is her uncle?

   ⬭ a. He waves at her.
   ⬭ b. He is painting.
   ⬭ c. He is wearing the clothes her uncle said he would be wearing.
   ⬭ d. He looks like him.
   ⬭ e. Somebody told her it was him.

5. How does the man initially react to the presence of the girl?

   ⬭ a. He is scared of her.
   ⬭ b. He tries to ignore her.
   ⬭ c. He embraces her.
   ⬭ d. He is angry with her.
   ⬭ e. He tries to help her.

6. 'Oh, my mistake, is it important to you to run around harassing strangers? I'm so sorry to inconvenience you.' (lines 51-52)
   In what tone is Wilson speaking here?
   - a. enthusiastic
   - b. apologetic
   - c. glum
   - d. melancholy
   - e. sarcastic

7. How tall is Wilson?
   - a. 5'3"
   - b. 5'5"
   - c. 5'7"
   - d. 6'
   - e. 7'

8. Why is Trevor described as having 'embarrassed eyes' (line 64)?
   - a. Wilson has seen him eavesdropping.
   - b. There is a young girl in a private jazz club.
   - c. His trousers have fallen down.
   - d. He is bald.
   - e. He is in the way.

9. What does Trevor note is peculiar about Wilson's behaviour?
   - a. He is annoyed by the girl.
   - b. He apologises to the girl.
   - c. He suddenly stops acting rudely.
   - d. He keeps trying to leave.
   - e. He acknowledges Trevor.

10. How many excuses does Wilson give in order to explain his surly manner?
   - a. zero
   - b. one
   - c. two
   - d. three
   - e. four

11. Which of the reader's senses are engaged by the phrase '...a velvety melody...' (line 85)?
    1. sight
    2. touch
    3. smell
    4. hearing

    a. 1 and 2
    b. 1 and 3
    c. 2 and 3
    d. 3 and 4
    e. 2 and 4

12. Which of the following is the best synonym for the word 'proverbial' (line 91)?
    a. old-fashioned
    b. familiar
    c. uncomfortable
    d. authoritative
    e. stylish

13. 'The room was dark and smoky, a smatter of people spread across it, each individually lounging in a chair, or else tapping their fingers to the sound of jazz.' (lines 6-9 and 91-94)
    This sentence is used at the beginning and at the end of the passage. What effect does this repetition have?

    a. It shows how quickly things return to normal after Wilson's visit.
    b. It confuses the reader and causes a feeling of déjà vu.
    c. It shows the story going back in time.
    d. It shows that Wilson is dreaming.
    e. It is a publishing mistake.

14. How is the reader intended to feel at the mention of the 'winking, green light' (line 99)?
    a. elated
    b. surprised
    c. intrigued
    d. amused
    e. dejected

15. What genre of fiction is this story most likely to belong to?
    a. comedy
    b. fantasy
    c. romance
    d. science fiction
    e. mystery

BLANK PAGE

Tomorrow is a Patchwork (Test 9)

Marking Grid															
Question	1	2	3	4	5	6	7	8	9	10	11	12	13	14	15	Total
✓ or ✗																

Read the following instructions carefully:

1. You have 12 minutes to complete this test of 15 questions.

2. You are recommended to spend 5 minutes reading the text, and 7 minutes answering the questions.

3. Work as quickly and as carefully as you can.

4. When you have finished a page, continue straight on to the next page. Do not waste time.

5. You can write on the text itself, or use the available space on the question paper to do any working. However, only mark your final answer in the answer boxes.

6. Mark your answer using a pencil, by drawing a firm horizontal line in the box next to your chosen option.

7. To change an answer, rub out your original answer completely and then mark on your new choice.

8. If you cannot answer a question, go on to the next question.

9. When you have completed the paper, use the time remaining to go back to any questions you have missed out and check your answers.

Good luck!

Once you have completed each test and marked it using the answers at the back you can anonymously go online and compare your child's performance relative to peers who have completed the same test(s) using our 11+ Peer Compare System™. Register at http://peercompare.elevenplusexams.co.uk/ and then activate the access code printed on the front inside cover of this book.

'Tomorrow is a Patchwork'

MONDAY 1st July, 2084

Dear someone (anyone?),

Whatever the government pamphlets, radio advertisements, news features or official reports claim, this programme is not 'the future of humankind'. If it
5   goes on, it will doubtless be the death of us all.

Today, my sister was summoned for her Aptitude Analysis. Mother was petrified, and took to whispering maths equations into her ear all night. Of course, Li Na bawled through it all, her tiny, spidery baby fingers wrapped around Mother's quivering thumb. It is clear that even two-week-olds have the
10   emotional intelligence to recognise anxiety in those close to them. While endearing, it is a dangerous mechanism; production of stress hormones in particular is detrimental to the brain's efficiency. Not only should Mother have remained calm, singing soothing melodies would have been the best way to prime Li Na's brain for the Analysis. Nevertheless, I can't blame Mother; she
15   was assigned Maths Researcher, so it's all she knows. She never learnt how to sing.

Mother's principal fear is that Li Na will be assigned something in the Physical Category. She has remarkably strong arms and legs and is in the perfect weight bracket for Beginners Combat. Mother knows the Boxers and the Martial
20   Artists lead difficult lives, if they can be called lives; you see them walking around the halls, blacker and bluer than ink, muscles bulging grotesquely from every angle, each with a swarming horde of bodyguards to protect them from injury and prevent them from smuggling any luxury items (chocolate bars, sweet fruits, cakes, biscuits) into the Athletes Department. I find the condition
25   of the under-fives group most unsettling. I can't even look.

Despite this, I'm not sure I agree that the Physical Category is the worst lot. Taking into account the long-term, the No-Hope Category is potentially the most feared. Most No-Hoper roles require only two years of training before beginning work, with no scope for career progression. I wouldn't like Li Na to
30   be a Train Driver or a Dustbin Girl or Cleaner before she had even reached one metre in height. I mean, no-one ever escapes from their assigned role, even

after thirty years of the job, but at least most don't start until after the age of six. The early entry assignations lead to a drawn-out, hellish existence. Still, as the government always says, *someone's* got to do those jobs.

35 I was fortunate, says Mother. She believes those in the Creative Category have it best, because the physical training is softer and the entry date is later. Especially for Writer-Linguists like me, where the bulk of the pure physical training is about speed, with a view to improving the rate of production - typing and editing mainly. The only physical dangers are that of repetitive
40 strain injury or damage to eye muscles. But the Optimum Healthcare Service will replace hands and eyes if necessary, so those problems are rarely truly debilitating.

I suppose Mother is correct; my vocation is less physically demanding, but the Knowledge Input course is more than intensive. It's been six years of twenty-
45 hour-a-day audio-visual inputting - all my six years of life blur into one never-ending film reel of sitting in purple rooms, my brain being moulded by alpha waves and reading, reading aloud, being read to, being read at. The first few years were particularly distressing, as they had not quite developed the right dosage per individual. I used to wake up in the middle of the night with a
50 searing pain in my head, scarlet streams of blood leaking from my ears and nose. It's not so bad now, but the memories remain. Educated humans never forget.

Tonight, my sleep shall be restless and broken. Tomorrow, we will discover Li Na's fate.

55 *And so we beat on, boats against the current, borne back ceaselessly into the past.*

Signed,

Wang Jing (six-years-old today)

Tuesday 2ⁿᵈ July, 2084

60 Dear someone (anyone?),

Li Na got assigned Dancer. She is in the Physical-Creative Category. I am relieved for her but Mother is devastated. She begins Physical Conditioning on Friday.

It matters not what someone is born, but what they grow to be.

65 Signed,

Wang Jing

Thursday 11th July, 2084

Dear someone (anyone?),

Today another Artist was found having a breakdown in the hallway. Incidents
70 like this are becoming more and more frequent in the Creative Category. The boy in question is six years of age, just a few months older than me. Rumour has it that he was found naked with the words 'I am not a robot' in acrylic paint across his body. He was crying and refused to see the Psychological Conditioner. They say he was due for release, though I have a feeling this
75 episode will cost him his 'freedom' - core modules of his training will inevitably be re-administered.

I was in the Nutrition Department taking my capsules when I heard. Incidentally, they have changed my diet programme. The doses are now one capsule of sodium, two of fat, three of fibre, three of protein, four vitamin and
80 two mineral. I sincerely hope I am not being used for gathering test data. They prefer to use children from the Creative Category as pique physical condition is not as necessary to optimal functioning in our fields. Perhaps the Artist boy was a test subject, which might explain why his brain malfunctioned.

It has been a long week. Purple-room days continue (today I covered 19th
85 century Portuguese literature) and the training is equally monotonous.

I thirst for paint and pens and pencils. I wish I knew how to make Visual Art, but all I know is words and grammar and stories. I wish I could paint my sadness and frustration instead of having to sift through hundreds of different vocabularies, only to find there is no real way to fully express how I feel. If only
90 I knew how to compose a piece like the Musicians. I have never even heard a

song, save the ringing of the bell that signals bedtime. I wonder how the Inventors and the Doctors feel, whose creative abilities are limited to science rather than expression. How do they describe their emotions, or do they simply weep at night and forever hold their peace?

95 The older I get, and the closer to job entry, I cannot help but feel that this system quashes more potential than it develops, and hampers more than it encourages.

I hope, or I could not live.

Signed,

100 Wang Jing

1. Why is each section of the text subtitled with a date?
   - a. They inform the reader when the author wrote each section.
   - b. They are newspaper articles.
   - c. The date should always be written at the top of any piece of work.
   - d. The author cannot think of any interesting subtitles.
   - e. They are diary entries.

2. Which of the following is the best synonym for the word 'bawled' (line 8)?
   - a. kicked
   - b. slept
   - c. wailed
   - d. bowled
   - e. gulped

3. Why was Wang Jing's mother's thumb quivering?
   - a. She was ill.
   - b. She was excited.
   - c. She had a lot of energy.
   - d. She was terrified.
   - e. She was exhausted.

4. Why did Wang Jing's mother not sing to Li Na?
   - a. She hated music.
   - b. Li Na hated music.
   - c. She thought singing produced stress hormones.
   - d. She had been forbidden from singing.
   - e. She had never learnt how to sing.

5. What type of word is 'blacker' (line 21)?
   - a. a noun
   - b. a comparative
   - c. a verb
   - d. an adverb
   - e. a conjunction

6. How many years of training do most No-Hoper roles require before they can start working?

   ⬭ a. one
   ⬭ b. two
   ⬭ c. six
   ⬭ d. twenty
   ⬭ e. none

7. What role has Wang Jing been assigned?

   ⬭ a. Maths Researcher
   ⬭ b. Dancer
   ⬭ c. Boxer
   ⬭ d. Artist
   ⬭ e. Writer-Linguist

8. 'Tomorrow, we will discover Li Na's fate.' (lines 53-54)
   What effect does this sentence have?

   ⬭ a. It creates humour.
   ⬭ b. It creates horror.
   ⬭ c. It creates suspense.
   ⬭ d. It creates confusion.
   ⬭ e. It creates sadness.

9. Which of the following is the best definition for the word 'devastated' (line 62)?

   ⬭ a. in a state of disbelief
   ⬭ b. fuming with anger
   ⬭ c. crumbled to pieces
   ⬭ d. feeling disappointed and let down
   ⬭ e. in a state of overwhelming shock or grief

10. '...he was found naked with the words "I am not a robot" in acrylic paint across his body.' (lines 72-73)
    Which of the following best characterises the boy's actions?

    ⬭ a. a practical joke
    ⬭ b. an art project
    ⬭ c. a crime
    ⬭ d. a protest
    ⬭ e. an attack

11. In what tense is the word 'refused' (line 73)?
- a. past tense
- b. future tense
- c. present tense
- d. future passive tense
- e. none of the above

12. What did Wang Jing really want to do?
- a. learn languages
- b. hear a song
- c. create art
- d. explore science
- e. work in a stationery shop

13. How does everyone know when to go to bed?
- a. A bell is rung.
- b. The lights are turned out.
- c. A song is sung.
- d. The heating is turned off.
- e. They are given bedtime cocoa.

14. What does Wang Jing think the Inventors and Doctors must struggle with?
- a. studying science
- b. describing their emotions
- c. drawing and painting
- d. learning languages
- e. getting jobs

15. When is this passage set?
- a. the present
- b. the future
- c. the past
- d. a timeless period
- e. a mixture of periods

Within the Red Ravine (Test 10)

Question	1	2	3	4	5	6	7	8	9	10	11	12	13	14	15	Total
Marking Grid																
✓ or ✗																

Read the following instructions carefully:

1. You have 12 minutes to complete this test of 15 questions.

2. You are recommended to spend 5 minutes reading the text, and 7 minutes answering the questions.

3. Work as quickly and as carefully as you can.

4. When you have finished a page, continue straight on to the next page. Do not waste time.

5. You can write on the text itself, or use the available space on the question paper to do any working. However, only mark your final answer in the answer boxes.

6. Mark your answer using a pencil, by drawing a firm horizontal line in the box next to your chosen option.

7. To change an answer, rub out your original answer completely and then mark on your new choice.

8. If you cannot answer a question, go on to the next question.

9. When you have completed the paper, use the time remaining to go back to any questions you have missed out and check your answers.

Good luck!

Once you have completed each test and marked it using the answers at the back you can anonymously go online and compare your child's performance relative to peers who have completed the same test(s) using our 11+ Peer Compare System™. Register at http://peercompare.elevenplusexams.co.uk/ and then activate the access code printed on the front inside cover of this book.

'Within the Red Ravine'

THERE was no smell. There was no wind.

I was suffocating, in the heat, in the arid air, under the unrelenting blaze of the mid-afternoon sun. Woozy, I had not tasted water for days, and my eyes were rolling and revolving searchingly in their sockets, unable to focus on my set destination. Though exhausted, I dragged one lead foot in front of the other, determined to reach the creek that I knew lay beyond. To bathe, to be clean and free from the flowing film of sweat smothering me, I knew would make everything better. I just needed to keep going. In order to persevere, I had devised a tactic of keeping close to the edge of the ravine so that at least one arm could find relief in the limited shade. At this time of day, I was staying to the west side, praying for the sun to accelerate its course and dip down into sweet darkness, behind the looming walls of my prison, allowing my red-crusted skin a few hours of repose.

Fat, wobbling tears tumbled from my lashes, yet none survived long, evaporating within milliseconds. Nora's name passed across my cracked lips over and over, though I tried to prevent it. "Nora, Nora, Nora…" I breathed, tormenting my own ears with anguish that only built, never died away. "Nora, come back."

Ceaseless in my mind were the replays of the scene. How she looked as I lost her, her frightened eyes and quivering cheeks, the last touch of her fingers against mine.

For a moment, my chest shuddered as I let out a terrific sob, my heart ricocheting heavily against the cage of my ribs. Of course, it was too physical for my body to bear, and I crumpled against the wall of earth to my left, inhaling hot dust and shaking with fatigue. "Nora…"

As I knelt on the ground, dizzy and on the verge of blackout, I began to feel a strange sensation against the crook of my neck. At first it was so unfamiliar it was painful, but then it started to soothe me. My mind whirred, struggling to make sense. "A breeze!" I realised after a few moments. Suddenly, I found strength in curiosity. I stood erect and twisted round to locate the source of the breeze. It was flowing through a small hole in the wall of the ravine. I placed my hand close to it, muscles taut with tension.

A real, true, blast of air was coming from that hole. I pressed my hand to it, hard this time, as if I could drink up the cold air through the palm of my hand

35   and have it cool my entire body like a wave of ice. I pressed and I smiled and I was filled with happy energy. Ecstatic, I pushed with all my might against the hole in the wall, laughing and crying simultaneously.

My celebration was interrupted. I heard a loud CRACK and a gash appeared in the dry earth, which quickly disintegrated under the pressure of my fingers and

40   fell to the ground. The wall caved in on itself, crumbling apart, falling around me. I recoiled, a statue of fear, ready to be swallowed up and meet my fate. It was an apocalyptic scene, like the end of the world. I stepped forwards, ready to be engulfed.

Then, SMACK! I was hit with a gust of arctic air. I opened my eyes, which had

45   snapped shut at the first sign of trouble. What I saw and felt I could not process. I was stunned. There in front of me was a huge cave of black rock, empty and silent, and *cold.* I had stumbled across a pocket of *cold* air in a veritable desert! A cave concealed within a treacherous ravine... How was this possible?! Was I mad? Was I hallucinating?

50   The sweat on my body was now like a blanket of ice, causing a prickling sensation against my sunburnt skin. It felt wonderful, like being reborn. I was alive. With all of my senses lucid, I knew this was far from a hallucination. As I waded in, I felt needles of cold slice against my bare feet, but not unpleasantly. "Nora," I called out, delighting in the echo of my voice, in the comfort of the

55   cave. "Nora, I'm going to be ok!"

"AAAAAAAAAaaaaaaaaa!"

A loud, wrangled cry roared out from the depths of the cave and filled my defenceless ears. It was a high shriek, like a young girl wailing, dipping down at the end as if the sound was coming from a person falling down a deep well.

60   "AAAAAAAAAaaaaaaaaa ...!" It came again. A traumatic scene flashed once more before my eyes.

Before I could form a sensible, self-preserving thought, my legs started forwards, and I was racing, bounding towards the sound. The soles of my feet slapped against the floor as I hurtled into the shadowed passages of the cave

65   ahead, following the sound, brushing past clammy grey rocks and ducking to avoid hitting the low cave roof. My knees shook, unwilling to go on, but I pushed, magnetised by the blood-curdling "AAAAAAAAAAaaaaaaaaaa ...!"

that resounded powerfully all around me. The sound grew louder, and I saw, barely perceptible in the distance, the outline of a body curled up on the ground a few feet in front of me.

My breathing was shallow and desperate as I approached the figure; I slowed, heart thumping with anticipation. "Nora?" I whispered. I knew it could not be her. She was gone, gone, gone. But the sound...

I arrived at the body. About two feet in height, it was certainly too small to have been Nora. Its proportions were too deformed to even be human - the head too large, the rear an odd shape. It was moving ever so slightly, writhing as if in pain. I wanted to offer comfort, so I placed my hand gingerly on its middle and was surprised to encounter a scaly texture. Then as if to acknowledge my presence, the creature coughed raspingly, and a small spark of a flame flashed in the gloom, before fluttering to the ground as wisps of ash.

I leant closer, eyes wide, as the creature emitted another "Aaaaaa....." this time, feebler than before.

"What *are* you?" I murmured. I had seen all types of fantastical beings on my travels with Nora; I had dined with elves, ridden pure-breed centaurs and fought werewolves in the charmed light of the full moon. But my instinct told me this was something more special, hidden away in a cave in a ravine in a desert.

Resting both my hands gently on its pulsing abdomen, I craned my neck to peer at its face. Its eyes were shut, its cheeks and forehead charred and grubby. Something in the cluttered cavern of my memory stirred, and I understood.

"Hello, little dragon. What are you doing here?"

1. Which of the following best describes the setting in the opening paragraph?
   - ⬭ a. torturous
   - ⬭ b. serene
   - ⬭ c. baffling
   - ⬭ d. enchanting
   - ⬭ e. bothersome

2. At what time of day does the story begin?
   - ⬭ a. dawn
   - ⬭ b. mid-morning
   - ⬭ c. midday
   - ⬭ d. afternoon
   - ⬭ e. dusk

3. What motivated the protagonist to keep moving through the ravine?
   - ⬭ a. He was looking for Nora.
   - ⬭ b. He was being chased.
   - ⬭ c. He was competing in a race.
   - ⬭ d. He wanted to reach the end before nightfall.
   - ⬭ e. He wanted to reach the creek beyond the ravine.

4. '...free from the flowing film of sweat smothering me...' (line 7)
   What literary technique is prevalent in this phrase?
   - ⬭ a. onomatopoeia
   - ⬭ b. alliteration
   - ⬭ c. rhyme
   - ⬭ d. personification
   - ⬭ e. irony

5. What was the primary reason for the protagonist's extreme sadness?
   - ⬭ a. He was lost.
   - ⬭ b. He was in pain.
   - ⬭ c. He was missing Nora.
   - ⬭ d. He was thirsty.
   - ⬭ e. He was overheated.

6. Why was the sensation of the breeze against his neck initially painful for the protagonist?

   ⬭ a. It was a scalding temperature.
   ⬭ b. He had a cut on his neck.
   ⬭ c. It was a particularly strong gust of air.
   ⬭ d. He had not felt any wind for a long time.
   ⬭ e. He was allergic to wind.

7. What type of words are 'CRACK' (line 38) and 'SMACK' (line 44)?

   ⬭ a. verbs
   ⬭ b. onomatopoeia
   ⬭ c. misspellings
   ⬭ d. adjectives
   ⬭ e. salutations

8. Which of the following is the best antonym for the word 'lucid' (line 52)?

   ⬭ a. absent
   ⬭ b. clear
   ⬭ c. amplified
   ⬭ d. altered
   ⬭ e. hazy

9. 'A traumatic scene flashed once more before my eyes.' (lines 60-61)
   To what scene is this sentence referring?

   ⬭ a. his walk through the ravine
   ⬭ b. the moment when he lost Nora
   ⬭ c. the moment when the wall of the ravine collapsed
   ⬭ d. a scene from a film
   ⬭ e. a vision of the future

10. Why does the protagonist follow the sound without thinking?

   ⬭ a. A part of him thinks it is Nora.
   ⬭ b. He is curious.
   ⬭ c. The sound is a spell that enchants him.
   ⬭ d. He knows it is a dragon.
   ⬭ e. He has no common sense.

11. According to the protagonist, why did the creature cough?

     ▢ a. to scare him

     ▢ b. to burn him

     ▢ c. to light up the cave

     ▢ d. to acknowledge his presence

     ▢ e. to fake illness

12. '...the cluttered cavern of my memory...' (line 90)
    What type of phrase is this?

     ▢ a. a simile

     ▢ b. a metaphor

     ▢ c. a riddle

     ▢ d. an insult

     ▢ e. an idiom

13. How does the protagonist behave towards the dragon?

     ▢ a. angrily

     ▢ b. fearfully

     ▢ c. caringly

     ▢ d. nastily

     ▢ e. indifferently

14. What type of narration is used in this passage?

     ▢ a. 3rd person, present tense

     ▢ b. 3rd person, past tense

     ▢ c. 3rd person, mixed tense

     ▢ d. 1st person, present tense

     ▢ e. 1st person, past tense

15. What genre does this story belong to?

     ▢ a. romance

     ▢ b. historical fiction

     ▢ c. fantasy

     ▢ d. detective fiction

     ▢ e. adventure

BLANK PAGE

FIRST PAST THE POST®

COMPREHENSIONS
Contemporary Literature
Book 2
Tests 1-10

Answers

Once you have completed each test and marked it using the answers at the back you can anonymously go online and compare your child's performance relative to peers who have completed the same test(s) using our 11+ Peer Compare System™.

Register at http://peercompare.elevenplusexams.co.uk/ and then activate the access code printed on the front inside cover.

Test 1 - Flynn

Question	Answer	Source of Answer
1	D	Knowledge of vocabulary required. The word 'eager' means keenly expectant or interested. A synonym is a word that means the same, or nearly the same, as another word. Therefore, the option here that is the best synonym for 'eager' is 'keen'.
2	B	Reader's personal judgement required. Refer to the quoted text within the context of the passage to help form an opinion as to how Fran was feeling. 'Satisfied and grinning…' suggests the best option is that she was feeling triumphant and pleased.
3	C	Knowledge of literary techniques required. The quoted phrase is an example of a simile. A simile is a phrase that makes a comparison between two different things through a connective word such as 'like' or 'as'.
4	E	Refer to lines 24-25: '…the greatly anticipated biscuit break that she had been promising herself for the last mile.'
5	A	Refer to lines 15-16: 'Fran glanced back, at the path where her father had just reached the bottom of that small yet onerous slope that led to where she now proudly stood….' and to lines 25: '…she called to her father who was just breaching the top of the hummock.'
6	A	Reader's logical inference required. Refer to the phrases '…in the crisp morning air' (line 28) and '…her morning's achievement' (line 34) to make a decision as to what time of day it was when they stopped for the biscuit break. These phrases imply that it was the morning.
7	D	Refer to lines 30-31: '…he pulled out his camera and began adding to the already vast collection of pictures he'd taken that morning.'
8	B	Knowledge of literary techniques required. The quoted phrase is an example of alliteration. Alliteration is the repetition of the same sound at the beginning of adjacent or closely connected words, or in stressed syllables.
9	D	Knowledge of grammar required. The word 'wildly' is an example of an adverb as it is describing the verb 'shouted'. An adverb is a word that describes a verb, adjective or other adverb.
10	C	Knowledge of vocabulary required. The word 'futile' means pointless or useless. Therefore, the best option is 'incapable of producing a useful result'.
11	E	Reader's logical inference required. Refer to the phrases '…delved frantically into her bag to retrieve her phone and the card of emergency numbers…' (lines 76-77) and '…the operator of the mountain rescue dog association…' (line 90) to make a decision as to what plan Fran has. These phrases imply that option 'e' is the most likely.
12	B	Reader's personal judgement required. Refer to the description of the voice in lines 88-89 to help form an opinion as to which of the options best describes the operator's voice. Words such as 'calm' ' and 'level-headed' imply that option 'b' is the best description.
13	E	Reader's personal judgement required. Refer to the referenced descriptions of the clouds to help form an opinion as to how the clouds have changed. Words such as 'soft, pillowy' (line 6) and 'amicable' (line 14) imply that the clouds were pleasant at first, whilst words such as 'menacingly' (line 99) and 'malicious' (line 100) imply that they became threatening as the passage progressed.
14	A	Reader's logical inference required. Refer to lines 102-103: '…raindrops began to fall…sticking Fran's clothes to her cold skin…' to make a decision as to what the 'damp, cold sensation' (line 112) was. This phrase implies that it was due to rain falling on her clothes.
15	A	Reader's personal judgement required. Refer to the description of Flynn's arrival in lines 107-111 to help form an opinion as to how the reader is intended to feel. Words such as 'affectionately' (line 108), 'merry' (line 109) and 'friendly' (line 110) imply that the reader should feel happy and relieved.

Test 2 - Life at Nearly Six

Question	Answer	Source of Answer
1	D	Refer to lines 3-4: '...I'm extra mature from having to take care of my little brother.'
2	A	Knowledge of the English language required. The sentence 'Boys will be boys.' is an example of a saying. A saying is a short, well-known expression that generally offers advice or wisdom.
3	B	Refer to lines 14-15: '...I think he just means that it's because he is old and wrinkly.'
4	E	Refer to lines 21-22: '...speedy typing on the keyboard so it sounds like rain pat-a-pat-ing on the window.'
5	C	Refer to lines 32-33: 'Daddy is nearly always happy...I only ever saw him cry once...'
6	B	Reader's logical inference required. Refer to lines 40-41: '...her eyes were a little shimmery and sad-looking' to make a decision as to why her eyes were shimmery. The word 'sad-looking' (line 41) implies that this was because they were brimming with tears.
7	C	Knowledge of vocabulary required. The word 'scrunched' means crushed or squeezed into a smaller area. A synonym is a word that means the same, or nearly the same, as another word. Therefore, the option here that is the best synonym for 'scrunched' is 'squashed'.
8	D	Reader's personal judgement required. Refer to the quoted sentence within the context of the passage to help form an opinion as to how Isabella's father was feeling. As he was speaking slowly and reluctantly, it is likely that he was feeling distressed and uncomfortable.
9	A	Refer to lines 74-76: '"Yes, because the baby is nearly here!" "...Mummy went into hospital today and...in fact, now you have a lovely, cute baby brother..."'
10	E	Reader's logical inference required. Refer to the quoted text within the context of the passage to make a decision as to why Isabella's father didn't finish his sentence. As the following sentence is 'He stopped again, and blew his nose.' (line 88), it can be inferred that he was overcome by grief.
11	A	Reader's logical inference required. Refer to the text between lines 47-101, paying particular attention to what Isabella's father says and does, to make a decision as to why he did not say 'Your Mummy is dead.' His general attitude throughout this passage, as well as sentences such as '...I need you to listen quietly...so that I can explain in the best way possible.' (lines 58-60), imply that he is trying to be sensitive, so option 'a' is the best.
12	D	Reader's personal judgement required. Refer to the quoted text within the context of the passage to help form an opinion as to how well Isabella understands the situation. The fact that Isabella thinks that her mother can come back to see them implies that she has not understood what has happened.
13	E	Reader's logical inference required. Refer to the words 'love' (lines 50 and 79) and 'honey' (lines 58 and 89) within the context of the passage to make a decision as to why Isabella's father uses these words. As he is trying his best to break bad news in a sensitive way, it is most likely that he is being affectionate.
14	C	Reader's logical inference required. Refer to the text as a whole to make a decision as to why the author has used simplistic language. As the passage is narrated by Isabella, who is only five years old, it is most likely that the author is trying to mimic the voice of a young child.
15	B	Knowledge of grammar required. As the pronoun 'I' and the possessive pronoun 'my' are used throughout the passage, it is written in 1st person narrative. The narrator also frequently gives opinions such as 'I think my daddy is the smartest daddy in the world.' (line 17).

Test 3 - Miss Fortune's Galley

Question	Answer	Source of Answer
1	D	Reader's logical inference required. Refer to the description of Suzy's hair in lines 2-3 to make a decision as to what colour it is. The fact that it is compared to 'scarlet tongues of fire' (line 3) implies that it is red as 'scarlet' is a shade of red.
2	C	Knowledge of literary techniques required. The quoted phrase is an example of a simile. A simile is a phrase that makes a comparison between two different things through a connective word such as 'like' or 'as'.
3	E	Refer to lines 7-9: '...her full captain's kit, which included her most officious tricorn hat and a long, navy, billowing coat secured with a belt across the waist.'
4	E	Reader's logical inference required. Refer to the phrases 'Mornin', bucko' (line 13) and '...yer a right merry wench this mornin'!' (line 18) to make a decision as to what time of day it is. From these phrases it can be inferred that it is the morning.
5	A	Reader's logical inference required. Refer to the quoted text in the context of the passage to make a decision as to why Jack had colour 'rising in his face' (line 22). The word 'hastily' (line 21) implies that he was embarrassed.
6	A	Reader's logical inference required. Refer to the quoted text within the context of the passage to make a decision as to why Suzy's teeth are different colours. The most likely explanation is that some are rotten and some have been replaced with fake ones.
7	D	Refer to lines 35-39: '...Suzy at the helm...Jack had successfully roused One-Eyed Nick...Crabby Titchson and Anne Rackham...the troublesome trio of Mad George, Bonny Bess and Will de Sang...'
8	B	Refer to line 50: 'The cabin boy and the capt'n...'
9	D	Refer to lines 48-50: '"...we all know ye'd go bow-legged for our Suzy Smythe," sniggered Will. "The cabin boy and the capt'n, whoever heard of such a tale?"'
10	C	Reader's personal judgement required. Refer to the referenced text to help form an opinion as to how the atmosphere changes. Words such as 'magnificent' (line 58) and 'laughter' (line 62) imply that the atmosphere was happy at first, whilst words such as 'darkening' (line 67), 'grim' and 'deathly' (line 68) imply that the atmosphere became more eerie as the paragraph progressed.
11	B	Refer to lines 62-63: 'So wrapped up were they in their dances and their laughter, that they didn't notice the air getting colder...'
12	E	Refer to lines 72-74: 'Her skin prickled with cold, and she drew her coat desperately around her to retain what little body heat she had left.'
13	D	Reader's personal judgement required. Refer to the song in lines 83-90 and lines 95-97 to help form an opinion as to which of the options best characterises it. The repeated line 'Oh, poor old man, your horse will die' implies that the song is best described as chilling.
14	E	Refer to line 101: 'They're awful singers, by gum. 'S all out o' tune...'
15	A	Refer to lines 117-118: ''Cause only ghosts can't never sing in tune.'

Test 4 - Safety

Question	Answer	Source of Answer
1	C	Knowledge of literary techniques required. The quoted phrase is an example of alliteration. Alliteration is the repetition of the same sound at the beginning of adjacent or closely connected words, or in stressed syllables.
2	A	Knowledge of vocabulary required. The word 'exasperated' means intensely irritated or annoyed. A synonym is a word that means the same, or nearly the same, as another word. Therefore, the option here that is the best synonym for 'exasperated' is 'infuriated'.
3	B	Refer to line 16: '...drowsily munching on acacia leaves.'
4	D	Refer to lines 28-29: '...perhaps he was lonely up in the sky with no herd to keep him company.'
5	E	Reader's personal judgement required. Refer to the referenced text to help form an opinion as to which of the options best describes Toto's mother's breathing. The words 'regular rhythm' and 'permanent' (line 33) and 'faithfully' (line 36) imply that her breathing is best described as reliable.
6	E	Refer to lines 47-49: 'She turned her head eagerly, anticipating the arrival of a gazelle or a giraffe, anything that might cause even a trivial drama to unfold that she could watch...'
7	C	Knowledge of grammar required. The word 'anxiety' is an example of an abstract noun. A noun is a word that denotes a person, place, thing, animal or idea. Abstract nouns are words that denote concepts or ideas.
8	A	Refer to lines 61-62: 'An impertinent crack broke out from under her foot as a large, audacious branch gave way under her massive weight...'
9	C	Knowledge of vocabulary required. The word 'malice' means spitefulness and bad intentions. Therefore, the best option is 'a desire to harm someone or something'.
10	B	Reader's personal judgement required. Refer to the quoted phrase within the context of the passage to help form an opinion as to how the members of the herd might have been feeling. Words such as 'alarm' and 'terror' (line 74) imply that they might be feeling frightened.
11	D	Knowledge of grammar required. The tense of a sentence is usually indicated by the tense of the main verb. The main verb in this sentence is 'lurched' (line 78). As this verb is in the past tense, the sentence is in the past tense.
12	E	Refer to lines 85-87: '...sending a cloud of angry, red dust high into the air, filling his eyes and forcing them to snap shut...'
13	A	Reader's logical inference required. Refer to the referenced description in lines 93-96 within the context of the passage to make a decision as to what the 'two-legged creatures' are. The most likely explanation is that they are humans with guns who are hunting the elephants: '...metallic sticks pointed forwards, some letting off bright sparks as they sent ear splitting cracks ...'
14	E	Refer to lines 105-106: 'His mother's great, majestic head hit the ground with a heavy, thud, shaking her large ears and sending vibrations down her long trunk.'
15	E	Knowledge of grammar required. The word 'clumsily' is an example of an adverb as it is describing the participle 'stumbling'. An adverb is a word that describes a verb, adjective or other adverb.

Question	Answer	Source of Answer
1	B	Reader's logical inference required. Refer to the quoted phrase within the context of the passage to make a decision as to what this description means. The word 'ivory' is often used as a shade of white, so option 'b' is the best.
2	E	Knowledge of vocabulary required. The word 'protocol' means an established procedure. Therefore, the best option is 'the official set of rules that govern a particular situation'.
3	A	Refer to lines 6-8: '...the skeletal albino man behind the reception desk...he was the new administrator.'
4	C	Reader's logical inference required. Refer to the quoted words within the context of the passage to make a decision as to why they are printed in italics. Rafe's attitude during this speech is very assertive and confident, so the most likely explanation is that he said these words with emphasis.
5	A	Reader's personal judgement required. Refer to the description of Louis' reaction in lines 20-21 to help form an opinion as to which of the options best describes his reaction. The word 'unfazed' (line 20) and the phrase '...continued...without giving Rafe a second glance' (lines 20-21) imply that his reaction is best described as indifferent.
6	D	Reader's personal judgement required. Refer to the quoted sentence within the context of the passage. The idea that Rafe could 'smell success' (line 29) implies that he is feeling optimistic.
7	B	Refer to lines 31-33: 'As he coasted through town in his shiny, new toy (a BMW 7 Series), Rafe turned the case over in his mind.'
8	E	Refer to line 39: 'Cover details: CIA agent Michael Maguire...'
9	B	Knowledge of vocabulary required. The word 'monochrome' means black and white, or in varying tones of one colour. An antonym is a word that means the opposite of another word. Therefore, the option here that is the best antonym for 'monochrome' is 'colourful'.
10	A	Refer to lines 52-53: '...the material mostly obscured by cascading curls of long, black hair...'
11	C	Knowledge of literary techniques required. The quoted phrase is an example of alliteration. Alliteration is the repetition of the same sound at the beginning of adjacent or closely connected words, or in stressed syllables.
12	E	Refer to lines 71-73: 'Her accent, Rafe noted, was mostly anglicised, but she had a vague hint of a Russian-influenced pronunciation crept around the vowel sounds. '
13	C	Refer to lines 81-83: '...it's just that I haven't seen him in what, must be over ten years now! And since I was on this side of the Atlantic, I thought I'd just hop on over for an afternoon.'
14	B	Knowledge of grammar required. The word 'against' is an example of a preposition. A preposition is a word that links two elements of a sentence by providing information about their relationship in space or time.
15	D	Reader's personal judgement required. Refer to the text as a whole to help form an opinion as to what genre of book this passage is likely to come from. The passage contains no references to mystical lands or creatures, and so is unlikely to come from a fantasy book. It contains no references to advanced technology, and so is unlikely to come from a science fiction book. It is neither funny nor classical in nature, and so is unlikely to come from a humorous or classical book. Therefore, the most likely option is mystery.

Test 6 - The Great Wave

Question	Answer	Source of Answer
1	D	Readers' personal judgement required. Refer to the description of the wave in lines 1-6 to help form an opinion as to what impression is given. Phrases such as '...breathed out a dejected sigh...' (line 5) imply that he is depressed.
2	A	Reader's personal judgement required. Refer to the opening paragraph to help form an opinion as to what sort of atmosphere is created. Phrases such as '...recoiling under the empty gaze of the night' (line 1), '...cloudless sky' (line 4) and '...babbling cruelly' (line 6) imply that the setting is eerie and melancholic.
3	E	Refer to lines 13-14: '...accompanied by the occasional drop of salty water. The little boy ran and choked out tears...'
4	B	Refer to lines 29-30: 'The boy, suddenly aware that he was not breathing, flailed his way to the water's surface...'
5	C	Reader's logical inference required. Refer to the quoted text within the context of the passage to make a decision as to what the boy understood. The fact that he was 'vigilant for any sign of a person' (lines 34-35) implies that he understood that the voice had come from under the water.
6	D	Refer to line 48: 'But his curiosity weighed him down, and back he sank...'
7	C	Refer to line 58: '...drawing his knees towards him for warmth.'
8	E	Refer to line 74: 'I was crying because the other children wouldn't let me chop the wood.'
9	A	Reader's personal judgement required. Refer to the description of the dawn in lines 78-83 and to the opening paragraph and compare the two to help form an opinion as the how the mood has changed. Words such as 'joyfully' (line 79), 'golden' (line 82) and 'energy' (line 83) imply that the mood is much happier than that described in the opening paragraph by words such as 'dejected' (line 5).
10	B	Refer to lines 98-101: 'The fish laughed. "Ohhh, I am just terrified." "I'm shaking in my scales!" This was enough. The wave began to pour out angry tears.'
11	D	Knowledge of literary techniques required. The quoted phrase is an example of a metaphor. A metaphor is a phrase that describes something by claiming that it is the same as an otherwise unrelated object.
12	E	Knowledge of literary techniques required. The quoted phrase is an example of alliteration. Alliteration is the repetition of the same sound at the beginning of adjacent or closely connected words, or in stressed syllables.
13	A	Knowledge of grammar required. 'Suddenly', 'but', 'and' and 'as' are examples of conjunctions. A conjunction is a word that connects two words or phrases.
14	D	Reader's logical inference required. Refer to the text as a whole, paying particular attention to any mentions of the time of day to make a decision as to the time frame of the passage. As the opening paragraph refers to the 'empty gaze of the night' (line 1) and the piece ends soon after a description of the sun rising, it can be inferred that the rough time frame is a night.
15	E	Knowledge of literary techniques required. The non-human characters in this passage are often given human traits and characteristics; this is an example of personification. Personification is the representation of non-human things as human, or the attribution of human characteristics to them.

Test 7 - The Train to the Platform

Question	Answer	Source of Answer
1	D	Reader's logical inference required. Refer to the quoted text within the context of the passage to make a decision as to why her hair was 'plastered to her neck' (line 5). The phrase '...rain fell around her...' (line 5) implies that her hair was wet from the rain.
2	B	Reader's personal judgement required. Refer to the opening paragraph to help form an opinion as to which of the options best describes the atmosphere created. Words such as 'dark' and 'damp' (line 1), and 'deserted' (line 2) imply that the atmosphere is gloomy.
3	A	Refer to lines 11-12: '...gripping the hand rail tightly for fear of slipping down into the darkness.'
4	E	Knowledge of vocabulary required. The word 'restless' means unable to rest or relax. A synonym is a word that means the same, or nearly the same, as another word. Therefore, the option here that is the best synonym for 'restless' is 'agitated'.
5	C	Refer to lines 16-18: 'She heard a small, suppressed cough from the nearby bench and whipped her head around, alarmed at the first human sound that she had heard...'
6	E	Knowledge of literary techniques required. The quoted phrase is an example of a simile. A simile is a phrase that makes a comparison between two different things through a connective word such as 'like' or 'as'.
7	B	Knowledge of vocabulary required. The word 'reproving' means reprimanding or expressing disapproval. Therefore, the best option is 'she looked at it as if she wanted to tell it off.'
8	A	Knowledge of literary techniques required. The word 'pop' is an example of an onomatopoeia. An onomatopoeia is a word that phonetically imitates the sound it is describing.
9	D	Knowledge of literary techniques required. The doors and the train in the quoted phrase have been given human traits and characteristics; this is an example of personification. Personification is the representation of non-human things as human, or the attribution of human characteristics to them.
10	C	Reader's logical inference required. Refer to lines 45-47 to make a decision as to why the woman winced as she entered the carriage. The fact that 'she glanced down at the ground shooting past beneath her' (lines 46-47) implies that she was imagining falling beneath the train.
11	D	Knowledge of grammar required. The word 'humdrum' is an example of an adjective as it is describing the noun 'breathing'. An adjective is a word that describes a noun or a pronoun.
12	A	Reader's logical inference required. Refer to the quoted text within the context of the passage to make a decision as to why she 'snuck another brief glance' (line 68). Phrases such as '...suspicions began to prevail...' (line 67) imply that she suspected that the woman wasn't really reading.
13	E	Knowledge of vocabulary required. The word 'quell' means to suppress or put an end to; the meaning can also be inferred from the sentence in which the word is used (line 71) . An antonym is a word that means the opposite of another word. Therefore, the option here that is the best antonym for 'quell' is 'encourage'.
14	C	Knowledge of vocabulary required. The word 'alighted' means descended from a vehicle. Therefore, the best option is 'descend from a train or other form of transport'.
15	B	Refer to lines 78-96: '...it reluctantly began to pick up speed as it prepared to lug itself into the blackness...turned round to watch it disappear...the distant sound of a dog barking...abruptly followed by an angry voice calling its name.'

Question	Answer	Source of Answer
1	A	Reader's logical inference required. Refer to line 1: '...a breath of crisp February air...' to make a decision as to during which season the story takes place. The reference to February implies that it is winter.
2	C	Refer to lines 11-12: 'Trevor Scott inhaled, allowing the smell of his very own jazz club to envelope him...'
3	E	Refer to lines 19-21: 'In such a relaxed atmosphere he was the only one who managed to create a sense of tension...'
4	C	Refer to lines 40-41: ''Cause, you see, he rang the other day and said he would meet me here, and would be wearing red braces and grey slacks...'
5	B	Reader's personal judgement required. Refer to lines 36-49 to help form an opinion as to how the man initially reacted to the girl. The phrases '...not looking up' (line 37) and '...made no reply' (line 39) imply that he is trying to ignore her.
6	E	Reader's personal judgement required. Refer to the quoted text within the context of the passage to help form an opinion as to what tone Wilson is speaking in. It is most likely that he is speaking in a sarcastic tone of voice because, although he says that he is sorry, he doesn't really mean it.
7	D	Refer to line 55: '...bent his six-foot body into a mock bow.'
8	A	Reader's logical inference required. Refer to the quoted text within the context of the passage to make a decision as to why Trevor has 'embarrassed eyes' (line 64). As it says that Wilson 'caught sight of Trevor' (line 63) it is most likely that he has seen Trevor eavesdropping.
9	C	Refer to lines 67-68: 'It was peculiar, Trevor thought - The anger slid off Wilson Henry-Smith Danforth's face...'
10	D	Refer to lines 71-72: 'I'm so sorry - I've had a perfectly awful day at work and I'm tired and it's late...'
11	E	Reader's logical inference required. Think about the meaning of each of the quoted words to make a decision as to which senses are engaged. The word 'velvety' means feeling like velvet, and so engages the sense of touch. The word 'melody' means a sequence of notes that makes a tune, and so engages the sense of hearing.
12	B	Knowledge of vocabulary required. The word 'proverbial' means well-known so as to be stereotypical. A synonym is a word that means the same, or nearly the same, as another word. Therefore, the option that is the best synonym for 'proverbial' is 'familiar'.
13	A	Reader's personal judgement required. Refer to the quoted text within both of its contexts of the passage to help form an opinion as to the effect of its repetition. The phrase '...the memory of another brief encounter already fading from his mind' (lines 97-98) implies that the repetition shows how quickly things return to normal.
14	C	Reader's personal judgement required. Refer to the quoted phrase within the context of the passage, paying particular attention to how you feel as you read it, to help form an opinion as to how the reader is intended to feel. As there is no explanation provided for the 'winking, green light' (line 99), the reader is most likely to feel intrigued.
15	E	Reader's personal judgement required. Refer to the text as a whole to help form an opinion as to what genre of book this passage is likely to come from. The passage contains no references to mystical lands or creatures, and so is unlikely to come from a fantasy book. It contains no references to advanced technology, and so is unlikely to come from a science fiction book. It is neither funny nor romantic in nature, and so is unlikely to come from a comedy or romance. Therefore, the most likely option is mystery.

Test 9 - Tomorrow is a Patchwork

Question	Answer	Source of Answer
1	E	Reader's logical inference required. Refer to the referenced subtitles within the context of the passage to make a decision as to why each section is subtitled with a date. As there are a number of references to moments in time such as 'tonight' (line 53), 'tomorrow' (line 53) and 'today' (line 69), and the passage is written in the present tense, it is most likely that each section is a diary entry.
2	C	Knowledge of vocabulary required. The word 'bawled' means wept or cried noisily. A synonym is a word that means the same, or nearly the same, as another word. Therefore, the option that is the best synonym for 'bawled' is 'wailed'.
3	D	Refer to lines 6-7: 'Mother was petrified...'
4	E	Refer to lines 14-16: '...she was assigned Maths Researcher, so it's all she knows. She never learnt how to sing.'
5	B	Knowledge of grammar required. The word 'blacker' is an example of a comparative. A comparative is an adjective or an adverb that compares two or more nouns or verbs.
6	B	Refer to lines 28-29: 'Most No-Hoper roles require only two years of training before beginning work...'
7	E	Refer to line 37: 'Especially for Writer-Linguists like me...'
8	C	Reader's personal judgement required. Refer to the quoted sentence within the context of the passage to help form an opinion as to what effect it has. This short sentence conveys a significant piece of information and therefore creates a sense of suspense.
9	E	Knowledge of vocabulary required. The word 'devastated' means traumatised or in a severe state of grief. Therefore, the best option is 'in a state of overwhelming shock or grief'.
10	D	Reader's logical inference required. Refer to the quoted sentence within the context of the passage to make a decision as to which of the options best characterises the boy's actions. The best option is 'a protest'. A protest is a public demonstration expressing strong objection to a policy or action.
11	A	Knowledge of grammar required. The word 'refused' is in the past tense. This is indicated by the 'ed' on the end of the word and also by its surrounding context.
12	C	Refer to lines 86-88: 'I thirst for paint and pens and pencils. I wish I knew how to make Visual Art...I wish I could paint my sadness and frustration...'
13	A	Refer to line 91: '...save the ringing of the bell that signals bedtime.'
14	B	Refer to lines 91-93: 'I wonder how the Inventors and the Doctors feel...How do they describe their emotions...?'
15	B	Refer to the dates that subtitle each section of the passage: 'Monday 1st July, 2084' (line 1), 'Tuesday 2nd July, 2084' (line 59) and 'Thursday 11th July, 2084' (line 67).